A Primer of Oilwell Service, Workover, and Completion

First Edition

by Kate Van Dyke

published by
PETROLEUM EXTENSION SERVICE
The University of Texas at Austin
Continuing Education
Austin, Texas

in cooperation with
ASSOCIATION OF ENERGY SERVICE COMPANIES
Dallas, Texas

1997

———— Library of Congress Cataloging-in-Publication Data ————

Van Dyke, Kate, 1951
  A primer of oilwell service, workover, and completion/by Kate Van Dyke.—
1st ed.
    p.   cm.
  ISBN 0-88698-175-1
  1. Oilwell service and completion.   I. University of Texas at Austin.
Petroleum Extension Service.   II. Title.
  TN000.00000   1996

Catalog No. 3.60110
ISBN 0-88698-175-1

CONTENTS

FIGURES

FOREWORD

Much has changed in the well servicing and workover business since Petroleum Extension Service (PETEX) issued the third edition of *A Primer of Oilwell Service and Workover* in 1979. The oil industry has undergone a boom, a bust, and, recently, something of a recovery. What's more, as author Kate Van Dyke began researching and developing the new manuscript, it quickly became obvious that the book needed more information about well completions—so much more, in fact, that it warranted a title change. Too, technology has made considerable advances since 1979. Coiled tubing operations alone could account for a whole new book. Further, contractors and personnel have had to place even more emphasis on health, safety, and environmental concerns.

So, you will find many changes in *A Primer of Oilwell Service, Workover, and Completion.* One thing, however, that has not changed is PETEX's effort to make the book understandable for persons who are not familiar with the industry. The text explains technical terms and operations, and a glossary assists the reader with special terminology.

Petroleum Extension Service is wholly responsible for the content of this manual. While every effort was made to ensure accuracy, it is intended only as a training aid, and nothing in it should be considered approval or disapproval of any specific product or practice.

Ron Baker, director
Petroleum Extension Service

ACKNOWLEDGEMENTS

Special thanks go to Harold Foster, a retired well service and workover specialist who worked for many years in the industry. He helped the author, the photographer, and the artist by carefully reviewing their work. His encouragement and enthusiasm never waned throughout the development of this book. Kate Van Dyke wrote the book in her usual superlative manner. Debbie Caples designed and laid out the book; Kathryn Roberts expedited the publication of this work and worked with Harold to iron out difficulties; Kathy Bork edited the manuscript. Leslie Kell did the excellent artwork.

PETEX also thanks the many well service and workover companies without whose assistance this manual could not have been done. We would especially like to thank Pride Petroleum Services, Inc.; Cudd Pressure Control; Baker Tools; BJ Services; Yale E. Key Inc., all of which allowed, with the Permian Basin Petroleum Museum, photographs of their equipment, operations, or facilities. Pride Petroleum Services, in particular, went out of its way to ensure that the photographer could obtain the needed photographs.

I

INTRODUCTION

A newly drilled oilwell is not much more than a lined hole in the ground. When a drilling crew drills a well, they line it with large pipe called *casing*. They also cement the casing in the well (fig. 1.1). At this point in the well's life, it usually cannot produce oil and gas (*hydrocarbons*). The company that owns the well—the operator, or operating company— has to *complete* it. The operating

company completes the well by adding equipment and carrying out certain procedures that will allow the well to produce fluids (oil, gas, and water).

To complete a well, a crew usually installs a string of relatively small pipe—*tubing*— inside the well. Near the bottom of the tubing, crew members usually install a special sealing device called a *packer* and connect valves and metering devices on top of the well to control flow. Sometimes, crew members add a pump or another device to lift the oil out of the ground.

As wells produce over time, equipment fails and the rocks holding the hydrocarbons— the *reservoir*—cause problems. When problems with equipment and the reservoir occur, flow from the well either slows down or stops altogether. When this happens, the operator also has to repair and work on the well to bring it back to full production. The industry calls such repair and work *well servicing and workover*. The operating company customarily hires a well servicing and workover

company, or contractor, to do well repair and other remedial work.

Well servicing is maintenance work. It usually involves repairing equipment, but a servicing contractor may also add new equipment to restore the well's ability to produce hydrocarbons.

Workover includes any of several operations on a well to restore or increase production when a reservoir stops producing at the rate it should. Many workover jobs involve treating the reservoir rock rather than the equipment in the well.

Well servicing and workover are important because oil is the most heavily used energy source throughout the world. The U.S. Geological Survey has estimated that 70 percent of all hydrocarbons on earth have been discovered. Of these, 32 percent have been produced and consumed. The undiscovered 30 percent is most likely in small fields in difficult environments like the polar regions and under the seas and oceans. These environments are extremely expensive to drill in.

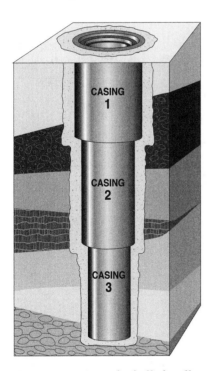

Figure 1.1. A newly drilled well lined with cemented casing

For these reasons, it is often more profitable to squeeze every possible drop of hydrocarbons from existing wells.

To understand what completion, service, and workover crews do, it helps to know the basic geology and mechanics of reservoirs and the fundamentals of drilling.

PETROLEUM RESERVOIRS

Geology

A petroleum reservoir is an underground source of oil or natural gas. It may be under land or under water (offshore). A reservoir is not like an underground lake trapped between two layers of rock. Instead, the hydrocarbons are inside a layer of porous rock, like water in a sponge. The reservoir rocks that contain hydrocarbons are sedimentary rocks. *Sedimentary rocks* are formed from existing rocks that eroded into particles (sediments). The sediments then settled somewhere and eventually became rock. Sedimentary rocks that hold hydrocarbons include sandstone, limestone, dolomite, or a combination of these.

A reservoir can take many shapes because of the movement of the earth over millions of years (fig. 1.2). In order to be commercially valuable, a reservoir must have the right shape and size. That is, it must lie in such a way that a large quantity of hydrocarbons can accumulate in it.

It must also be sealed off by impermeable rock above it so that the only escape for the hydrocarbons is through a well drilled into the reservoir. It must be large enough and hold enough hydrocarbons to make drilling worthwhile. It must be porous enough to contain the hydrocarbons (fig. 1.3).

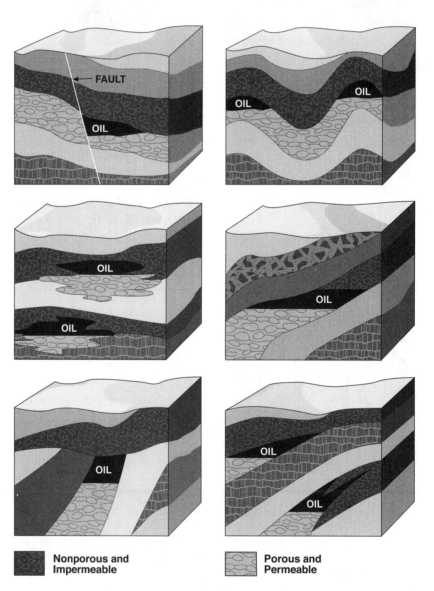

Nonporous and Impermeable

Porous and Permeable

Figure 1.2. A reservoir can take many shapes.

Figure 1.3. A rock is porous when it has many tiny spaces, or pores.

It must also be permeable—that is, the pores must be connected so that the fluids can flow through the rock by moving from one pore to another (fig. 1.4).

A *fluid* is any substance that will flow. A petroleum reservoir generally contains three fluids: oil, gas, and salt water. In some reservoirs, these fluids separate into different phases, like an oil and vinegar salad dressing before you shake it. Gas, the lightest-weight fluid, occupies the upper part of the reservoir rocks, in a *gas cap*. Water, the heaviest fluid, settles in the lower part, and oil lies between the gas and water (fig.1.5). Remember, though, that reservoirs vary a lot.

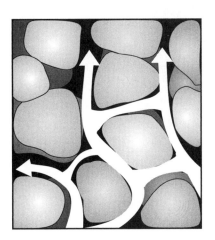

Figure 1.4. A rock is permeable when the pores are connected.

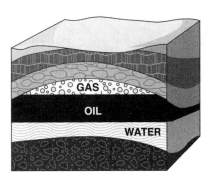

Figure 1.5. Reservoir fluids usually separate into layers of gas, oil, and water within porous rock.

For instance, some may contain mostly gas and water, with very little oil. Others may contain mostly oil and water, with very little gas. Sometimes, the gas is dissolved in the oil. This gas will come out of the oil when the fluids are produced.

Reservoir Pressure

All reservoir fluids are under pressure. Pressure exists in a reservoir for the same reason that pressure exists at the bottom of a swimming pool. Imagine a swimmer who decides to touch bottom. As he dives deeper, his ears begin to hurt because the pressure of the water is pressing against his eardrums. The deeper he goes, the greater the pressure.

Under normal conditions, the only pressure in a reservoir is the pressure caused by the water in and above it. Contrary to what might seem logical, all the rocks that lie over a reservoir normally do not create pressure in the reservoir. Usually, a reservoir's pores eventually communicate with the surface, where the surface releases the pressure. The reservoir rock itself may come out on the surface (an *outcrop*) or it may be adjacent to one or more formations that outcrop. In any case, the outcropping rocks act as a kind of relief valve for the weight of the formations overlying the reservoir.

When the reservoir has no connection to the surface, the heavy weight of the overlying rocks presses down and squeezes the reservoir. It is somewhat like blowing up a balloon, tying it off so that the air cannot escape, and then squeezing it. Since the air is confined, the pressure builds until it pops. Reservoirs do not pop, but the pressure can build to abnormally high levels.

Abnormally high pressure can also result from an artesian effect (fig. 1.6). In this case, the layers of rock, or formations, surrounding the reservoir trap the oil and gas, but allow the water below the oil to reach the surface some distance away. Since water seeks its own level, when the well provides an outlet for the reservoir, the water under it pushes the hydrocarbons up forcefully.

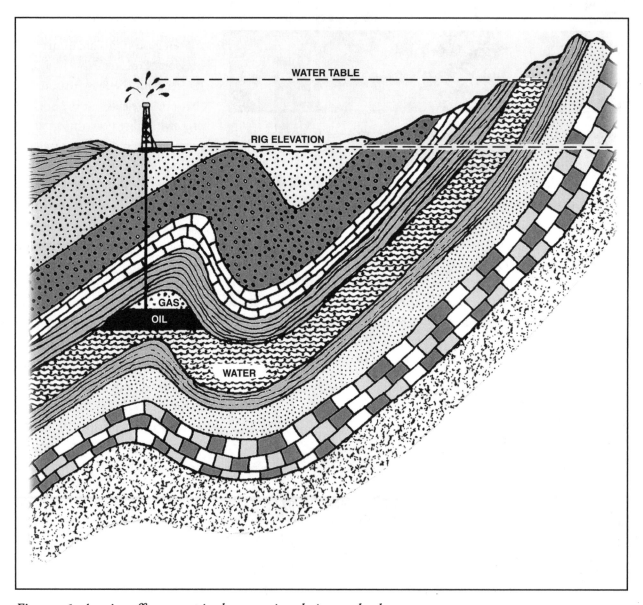

Figure 1.6. Artesian effect; water in the reservoir seeks its own level.

Reservoir Mechanics

After the well has been drilled and prepared to produce, the question is whether the oil will flow into the well and to the surface on its own. A single well can drain most of the oil from at least 80 acres (32 hectares). Many gas wells have drainage areas of at least 320 acres (128 hectares).

Some natural force within the reservoir must move the oil to the well from the outer reaches of the reservoir. In decreasing order of importance, the three natural forces that move the fluids in a reservoir are water, gas, and gravity.

Water Drive

In a well driven by water, water located beneath the oil in a reservoir is under pressure proportional to its depth. In other words, the deeper the water is, the higher the pressure. As soon as an opening occurs for the oil to move into (the well), water pressure forces the oil into it. Water is quite efficient at displacing oil from reservoir rock, and moving into pores the oil has left (fig. 1.7). The process is about the same as displacing oil in a tank by adding water at the bottom and letting the oil spill over the top.

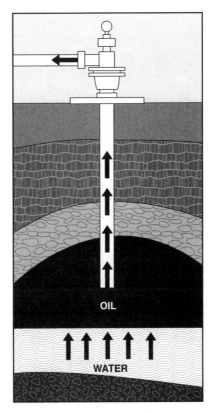

Figure 1.7. In a water-drive reservoir, water underneath the oil pushes it to the surface.

Water pressure remains high as long as an equal volume of water replaces the volume of oil withdrawn. Eventually, however, the water level rises to the point where the well is producing mostly water (fig. 1.8). When this happens, one solution is for a workover crew to plug up the bottom of the well and make holes in its sides higher up so that the rest of the oil will flow out.

Water drive is the most efficient natural drive. In a good water-drive reservoir, water can drive 50 percent or more of the oil out. As good a drive as water is, it still bypasses one half or more of the oil that is trapped in the rock's pores. The reason is very complicated, but it has to do with the way fluids move through pores and how they interact with each other as they move. In any case, the water sweeps past a fair amount of oil in the reservoir. This left-behind oil is a target for future technology.

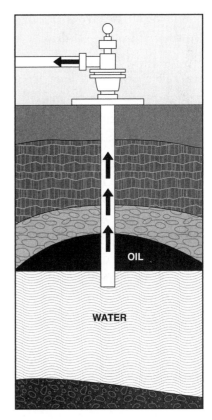

Figure 1.8. Eventually, the water level rises to fill the majority of the reservoir and the well produces mostly water.

Gas Drives

Gas drives work because the pressure of a gas is related to its volume, or the space it fills. A compressed gas, like air in a tire, has a high pressure. In other words, the air presses out against the walls of the tire with greater and greater strength as more air is forced into the space inside the tire. When air is released to the outside, it expands into the atmosphere and loses pressure; the tire goes flat.

There are two types of gas drive: dissolved-gas drive, and gas-cap drive. They are also called *depletion drives* because when the gas is gone, or depleted, the pressure that drives the oil out is gone. When the drive gives out, a service crew must add a pump or other artificial lift to the well to replace the natural drive.

A *dissolved-gas drive* works because some of the hydrocarbons in the oil are light enough that they become gaseous when the well releases pressure from the reservoir (fig. 1.9). This gas is like the bubbles in a soft drink. If you shake up a bottle of soda with the cap on, nothing happens.

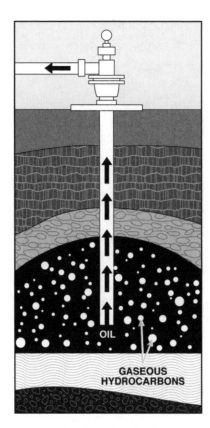

Figure 1.9. In a dissolved-gas drive reservoir, gas comes out of the oil, expands, and lifts oil to the surface through the well.

But when you uncap it, the carbon dioxide dissolved in the liquid becomes gaseous and liquid and gas foam up out of the bottle. Opening up the wellbore is like uncapping a soda bottle. The lighter hydrocarbons become gases and force the oil and gas to flow to the surface. Just as carbon dioxide gas in a soda bottle dissipates quickly after you uncap it, a dissolved-gas drive usually depletes quickly. The amount of oil recovered varies from 5 to 30 percent.

In some reservoirs, not all of the gas is dissolved in the oil; instead, it forms a cap on top of the oil. A reservoir that has a gas cap has a *gas-cap drive*. When the wellbore opens an escape route for the oil in the reservoir, the pressure of the compressed natural gas in the gas cap pushes oil into it. As the level of oil in the reservoir drops, the gas cap expands and continues to push oil into the well and up to the surface (fig. 1.10).

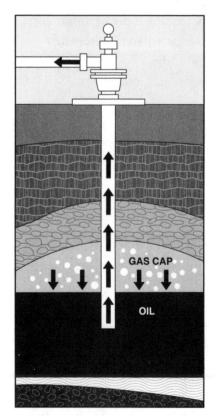

Figure 1.10. In a gas-cap drive reservoir, free gas in the cap expands and pushes down on the oil to move it to the surface.

The more space oil leaves in the porous reservoir rock, the more gas expands to take its place. Gradually, the gas loses pressure.

This drive works like a can of spray paint. A compressed, or pressurized, gas in the can sprays out a gas and paint mixture when the valve on top is opened. Eventually, pressure of the gas inside the can is no greater than the pressure of the air outside it, and it can no longer push out any paint left in the can.

The pressure of a gas-cap drive depletes more slowly than a dissolved-gas drive. From 20 to 40 percent of the oil in a reservoir may flow out before a gas-cap drive fails.

Combination Drives

More than one drive can work in a reservoir at the same time, and this is called a *combination drive*. One type of combination drive occurs when the oil has a gas cap above it and water below it. Both the gas cap and the water drive the oil into the well and to the surface. Another combination is dissolved-gas drive plus water drive.

Gravity Drainage

The least common type of reservoir drive is gravity drainage. The force of gravity is, of course, always at work in a reservoir. Usually, gravity pulls down the water so that it is underneath the oil. Water is heavier than oil, so gravity causes them to separate. However, in shallow, highly permeable, steeply dipping reservoirs and in some deeper, nearly depleted reservoirs, gravity makes oil flow downhill to the wellbore (fig. 1.11).

Figure 1.11.   In a gravity drainage reservoir, oil may flow downhill to the well.

DRILLING A WELL

To drill a hole that might easily be 3 miles (4.8 kilometres) or deeper into the earth is a monumental job. The collection of equipment and machinery that does it is a *rotary drilling rig* (fig. 1.12). Basically what happens when a rig drills a hole is that a boring device called a *bit* is pressed hard against the ground and turned. The rotating bit scrapes and gouges the rock out to make a hole. Above the bit, long sections of pipe, the *drill pipe*, screw together to connect the equipment in the hole to the equipment on the surface. The drilling crew keeps adding lengths of drill pipe as the hole gets deeper.

As the bit is turning, the rig pumps a special fluid down the drill pipe. This fluid is usually a liquid that has clay and chemicals in it. The clay and chemicals give fluid the properties it needs to do its job. When the fluid (usually called mud) reaches the bit, it jets out of it and moves the cuttings (rock fragments) away from the bit. With cuttings out of the way, the bit can cut fresh, undrilled formation. Mud then carries these cuttings up the hole to the surface. On the surface, equipment cleans the mud and the pump forces it back down the drill pipe.

Figure 1.12.   The rotary drilling rig is a collection of equipment and machinery that drills a well.

Whenever the bit is on bottom and turning, mud circulates to remove the cuttings.

A drilling rig is a sort of portable factory whose sole purpose is to make holes in the ground, or *make hole.* Once it drills a hole, the drilling crew breaks down the rig and moves it to another location to make another hole. (For more information about drilling, refer to the Petroleum Extension Service publication *A Primer of Oilwell Drilling.*)

Although the initial drilling of a well is done by a drilling crew, not a service or workover crew, some workover jobs require drilling to restore production.

Workover drilling uses the same type of equipment, although lighter and smaller, as primary drilling uses.

The drilling rig has four systems: a hoisting system for raising and lowering the bit; a system for rotating the bit; a system for circulating a fluid in and out of the hole; and a power system to run the other systems.

Hoisting System

The hoisting system of a drilling rig works like a windlass or winch. In a windlass, a drum, or spool, sits horizontally between two posts with one end of a rope attached to it (fig. 1.13).

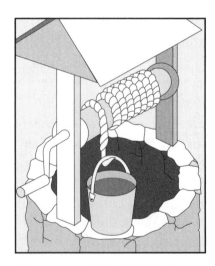

Figure 1.13.   The rig's hoisting system works like an old-fashioned windlass.

The other end of the rope is attached to something to be lifted, such as a bucket. Turning the drum with a crank winds the rope around the drum and lifts the bucket.

Figure 1.14 shows the main components of a drilling rig's hoisting system. The *drilling line* is the rope that does the same job as the rope on a windlass. It is made of woven steel wire.

The drilling line runs from a supply reel through an anchor to the top of the derrick or mast. The derrick is a familiar symbol of oilwells, a steel tower that may rise 120 feet (36 metres) in the air. Although oil people use the words "derrick" and "mast" interchangeably, a derrick is actually a permanent structure that must be disassembled piece by piece to remove it. A mast,

on the other hand, is portable. It folds or telescopes down into a size that can be transported by truck. The purpose of a mast or derrick is to support the drill pipe and rotary equipment, which in a deep well may weigh some 130 tons (118 tonnes).

The drilling line passes through a pulley (the *crown block*) at the top of the derrick, then down the center of the derrick to another pulley (the *traveling block*). The drilling line threads back and forth between the two blocks to gain several times the strength. The crown block does not move; it is anchored at the top of the derrick. The traveling block, as its name implies, travels up and down inside the derrick. It has a *drilling hook* below it from which the components of the rotating system hang.

After the drilling line makes its last pass through the crown block, it runs to a drum in the *drawworks*. As the drum rotates one way or the other, the drilling line spools on or off the drum. This raises or lowers the traveling block and the drill pipe hanging from it. The drawworks also contains machinery to control the drum—brakes, clutches, and a transmission.

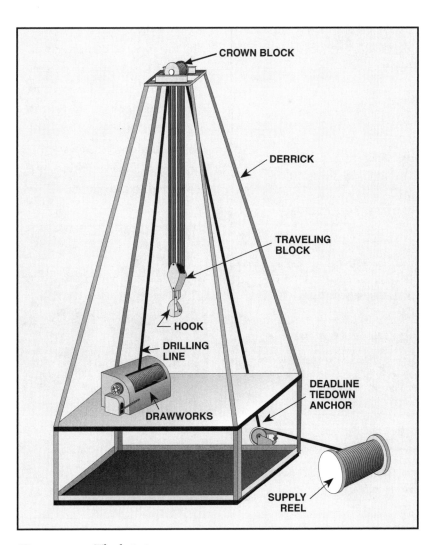

Figure 1.14. The hoisting system

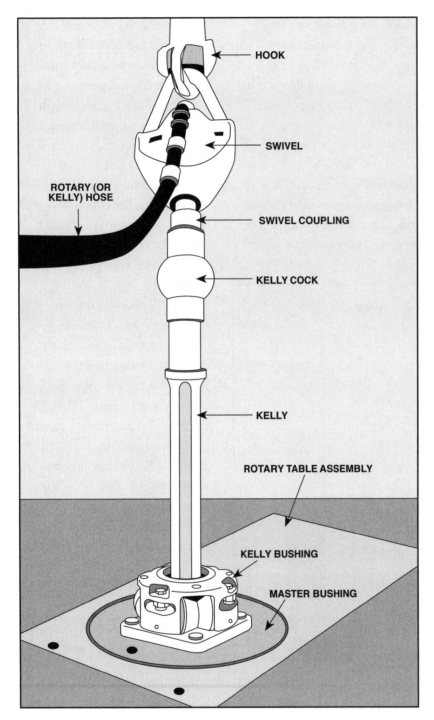

Figure 1.15. A conventional rotary system (drill pipe, drill collars, and bit are suspended in the hole below the rotary table.)

Rotating System

A conventional rotating system includes all the equipment that makes the bit turn (fig. 1.15). From the rig floor upwards, the conventional system consists of the rotary table and a master bushing plus the *drill stem*, which includes the swivel, a special type of pipe called a kelly, the kelly bushing, *drill pipe, drill collars*, and the *bit*.

Surface Equipment

The top piece of equipment in a conventional rotating system is the *swivel*, which hangs from the drilling hook on the bottom of the traveling block (fig. 1.16). Although the swivel does not rotate, it allows everything connected to it to rotate.

Figure 1.16. Traveling block, hook, and swivel

Attached to a threaded connection at the bottom of the swivel is the *kelly*. The kelly is a square or hexagonal pipe. A standard kelly is 40 feet (12.2 metres) long. The kelly fits into a corresponding square or hexagonal hole in a device called the *kelly bushing*. The flat sides of the kelly bushing hold onto the kelly so that they turn together (fig 1.17).

The kelly bushing in turn fits into a *master bushing* in the rotary table. A diesel or electric power source turns the rotary table, which rotates the whole drill stem up to the swivel and down to the bit. The rotary table can also hold gripping devices called *slips*. Slips suspend the drill pipe in the rotary table when the crew disconnects the kelly.

Top Drive

Sometimes rig owners replace the conventional swivel with a powered swivel called a *top drive*. The top drive hangs from the traveling block, in place of the conventional swivel (fig. 1.18).

A top drive has its own heavy-duty motor. The motor turns a threaded drive shaft that connects directly to the top of the drill stem to turn it. Rigs with top drives do not need a kelly, kelly bushing, or master bushing. They do retain the rotary table, but only as a place for the crew to suspend the drill stem.

Figure 1.18. The top drive hangs from the traveling block.

Figure 1.17. The kelly fits into the kelly bushing, which fits into the master bushing on the rotary table.

Downhole Equipment

The first section of drill pipe screws into the kelly or the top drive shaft. Many sections of drill pipe, or *joints,* screw together to reach near the bottom of the hole (fig. 1.19). Each joint is about 30 feet (9 metres) long. Depending on its diameter, a single joint may weigh 500 pounds (225 kilograms). The drilling crew *makes up* and *breaks out* (screws and unscrews) the joints of drill pipe with giant wrenches called *tongs.* If the rig uses a top drive, power tongs are built into the unit.

Below the drill pipe are special heavy pipes called *drill collars.* Drill collars have thick walls, and their purpose is to add weight to the drill stem. A 30-foot (9-metre) drill collar may weigh over 2,500 pounds (5,500 kilograms).

At the bottom of the drill stem is the bit. The sole purpose of all this rotary equipment is to apply weight to the bit and rotate it so that it can drill out the rock (fig. 1.20).

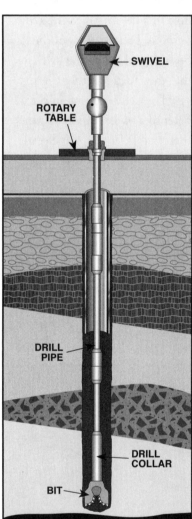

Figure 1.20. A drill bit is made up on the end of the drill string.

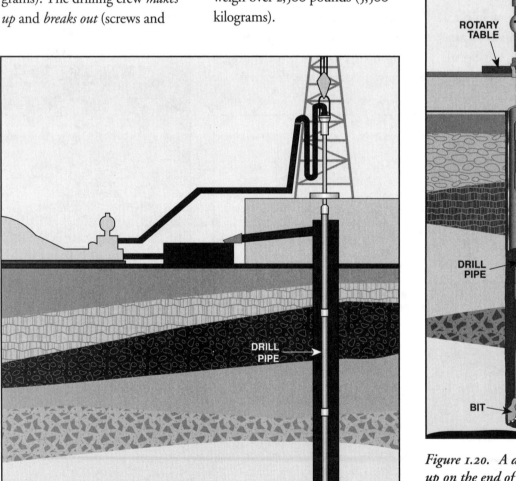

Figure 1.19. Joints of drill pipe are needed to reach the bottom of the hole.

Circulation System

As the bit is rotating, a special liquid called drilling fluid, or drilling mud, is pumped through the hollow drill stem and out of openings in the bit. Drilling mud is usually a mixture of water, clay, a weighting material, and a few chemicals.

Powerful pumps called *mud pumps* pick up drilling mud from steel tanks or pits where the mud is stored and send it through a line to a standpipe (fig 1.21). The standpipe stands vertically up one leg of the derrick. From the top of the standpipe, mud flows through the rotary hose to the swivel or top drive and down the drill stem.

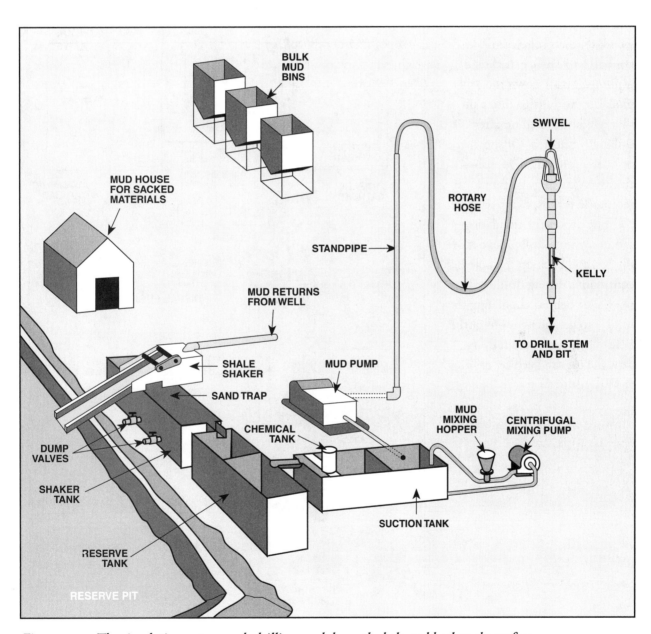

Figure 1.21. The circulating system sends drilling mud down the hole and back to the surface.

When mud shoots out of the rotating bit, it lifts fragments of rock (cuttings) that the bit has drilled. Then mud returns up the hole to the surface, carrying cuttings with it. A return line at the surface directs it either to a shale shaker, which screens out the cuttings, or straight to a tank that lets solids settle to the bottom. The cleaned mud is pumped back down the drill pipe; the cuttings go into a pit that will be covered up after drilling is finished. Offshore, or in environmentally sensitive areas, cuttings go into a receptacle for disposal elsewhere.

The process of circulating mud down the drill pipe, out of the bit, and back up the hole is continuous during drilling. The main idea behind circulating the mud is to get cuttings out of the hole. With cuttings out of the way, the bit can keep on drilling fresh, undrilled rock.

Power System

The power source, or *prime mover*, for the drilling rig is two or three huge diesel engines. These engines may run a series of drive shafts connected by chains, called a *compound*, that transmits power to the mud pumps, rotary, and hoisting system (fig. 1.22A).

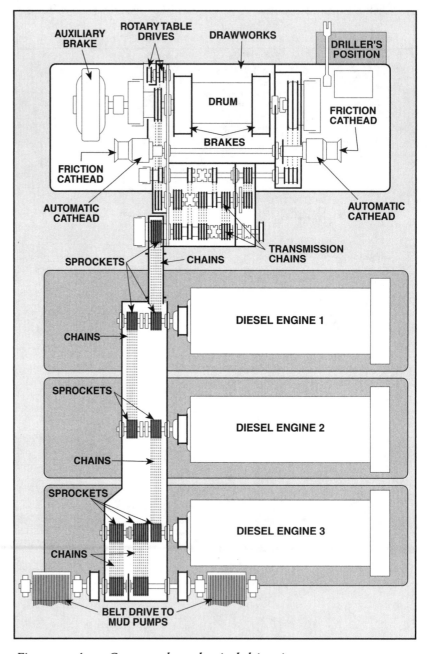

Figure 1.22A.   Compound, mechanical-drive rig

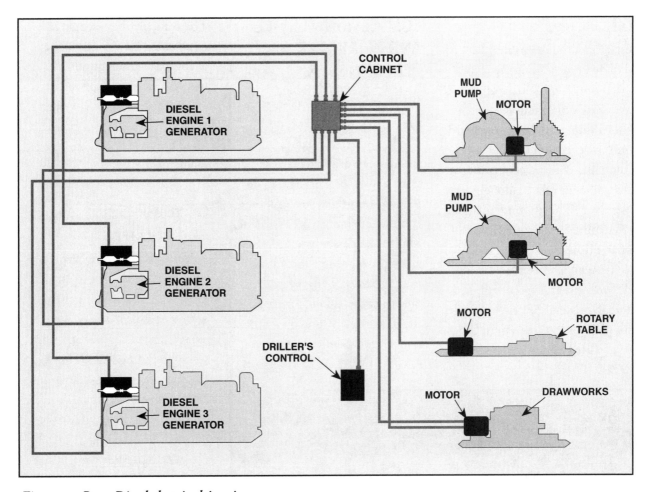

Figure 1.22B.   Diesel electric-drive rig

A rig powered through a compound is a *mechanical-drive rig*. Alternatively, the engines may provide power to generators that make electricity (fig. 1.22B). The electricity runs electric motors positioned near the systems needing power. This is an *electric-drive rig*.

Offshore Rigs

Offshore drilling rigs may be mobile units or permanent platforms. A mobile rig can be a floating unit, mounted on a barge, ship, or bottom-supported unit, that rests on the seafloor (fig. 1.23). A permanent platform is anchored to the seafloor in some way. The hoisting, rotating, circulating, and power systems of an offshore rig are the same as those on land rigs. The main difference is that space is limited, and all materials for drilling and supplies for the crews must be transported by ship.

COMPLETION, SERVICE, AND WORKOVER PERSONNEL

When an oil company leases the right to drill and produce a well, it hires companies that specialize in drilling, completion, service, or workover to do the job. Coordination of all these contract operations is the responsibility of a person who may be an employee of the oil company, the *company man* or *company representative*. Often, however, the oil company hires a *consultant*, an independent contractor.

The company representative is responsible for any number of wells, making sure production is maintained, preparing reports, testing, and so on. A consultant does the same job, but is usually hired only for a one-time assignment.

Completion, Service, and Workover Crews

A typical service or workover crew is made up of a *rig operator*, or *crew chief*, who is in charge of one or two *floorhands* and a *derrickhand*. The floorhands work on the rig floor. The derrickhand handles the upper end of the tubing or work string as it is being hoisted out of or lowered into the hole.

A completion crew is usually larger than a service or workover crew because completion involves several different jobs. A *toolpusher* is usually in charge of completion, over the rig operator.

Figure 1.23.   A drill ship is usually used to drill exploratory wells in deep, remote waters.

2

WELL COMPLETION

After a drilling crew has drilled a hole to the reservoir and lined the hole with pipe, it may or may not do the additional work needed to get the well into production. Sometimes crew members move on to drill another well, and a well servicing crew comes in to add the equipment needed to start the hydrocarbons flowing, or to complete the well.

Completion begins with installing tubing inside the casing to provide a flow path for oil and gas. The completion crew sets a seal called a packer to seal off the space between the tubing and the casing and installs a wellhead to control the flow of the reservoir fluids. Finally, the crew may install equipment such as a pump to lift oil to the surface, if natural drives cannot force it up.

CASING

Let's begin by reviewing the pipe, or casing, that lines the hole from the start of drilling to the end. Threaded couplings connect each joint of casing to form a *casing string*, which is the entire length of the casing. A cementing crew cements a string of casing in the hole as it is drilled; therefore, casing is not easily removable.

During drilling and completion, the crew runs several strings of casing into the hole. Each casing string fits inside the last, so each string is smaller in diameter than the one set before it (fig. 2.1). The first string is the *conductor casing*, a relatively short string (20 to 100 feet, or 6 to 30 metres) of large-diameter pipe that keeps the top part of the hole from caving in during drilling. The crew then drills below the conductor casing to just past the depth of the deepest fresh water in the formation.

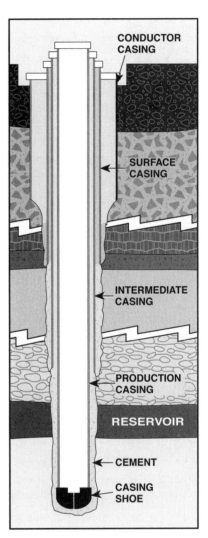

Figure 2.1. *Concentric strings of casing line the drilled hole.*

17

To prevent drilling mud and hydrocarbons from contaminating fresh water, which people use for drinking and irrigation, and also to keep loose sand or gravel from falling into the hole, the drilling crew runs *surface casing* inside the conductor casing. Surface casing runs from the bottom of this hole (the surface hole) to the surface, from 500 to 5,000 feet or so (150 to 1,500 metres).

The crew then continues drilling down to the oil reservoir. When the reservoir is very deep, the driller will often encounter troublesome formations, for example, one with high-pressure fluids in it. A high-pressure formation can cause oil and gas to blow out of the hole into the air, which is very dangerous and wasteful. By adjusting the properties of the drilling mud, a crew can successfully drill such formations. Later, however, as the hole passes through deeper formations, the mud they used to drill the high-pressure formation may no longer be suitable.

So, to make it possible to drill deeper, a casing crew runs another string of casing, called the *intermediate string,* and cements it. This string seals off the high-pressure zone or other troublesome formation. Intermediate casing fits inside the surface casing and runs from the bottom of the hole thus far to the surface.

Sometimes the drilling crew leaves after setting the intermediate casing, and a service crew sets the production casing. In most cases, the crew then drills to the final depth of the well, into the production zone. Sometimes, however, crew members will set a second intermediate string of casing if they encounter more troublesome formations above the production zone.

If this well is not the first well into the reservoir, the driller will go ahead with the first steps of completion to prepare the well to produce. In a wildcat (exploratory) well, however, now is the time for testing the well to determine whether a commercial amount of oil and gas is present.

When and if testing confirms the presence of hydrocarbons, the drilling or completion crew begins running the last string of casing, the *production casing* (also called the *oil string* or *long string*). Production casing usually runs from the bottom of the hole, or near the bottom, to the surface. It has a *casing shoe,* or *guide shoe,* at the end of the last joint. The casing shoe is a short, heavy, cylindrical section of steel filled with concrete and rounded on the bottom. It prevents the casing from snagging on irregularities in the borehole as it is lowered.

Then the driller pumps salt water into the hole to contain pressure in the reservoir and formation until the well is completed and ready to produce.

OPEN-HOLE AND PERFORATED COMPLETIONS

Open-Hole Completion

Production casing runs to the bottom of the hole and blocks off the production zone completely from the surrounding formation, or, rarely, stops just above the producing zone. If the casing stops above the producing zone and leaves the hole open, it is an *open-hole,* or *barefoot* (uncased), *completion* (fig. 2.2). Reservoir fluids simply flow from the formation into the hole. Almost always, however, casing runs to the bottom of the hole.

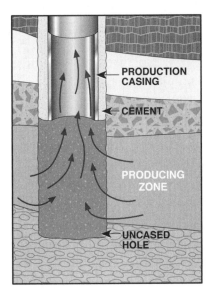

Figure 2.2. An open-hole completion allows reservoir fluids to flow into the uncased hole.

Perforated Completion

When the casing is run to the bottom of the hole, the hydrocarbons cannot get out of the reservoir and into the casing because the cement and casing walls seal it off. In this case, the crew perforates the casing by shooting holes in it so that the fluid can flow into the well. This is a perforated completion.

Crew members use a perforating gun, or perforator, to make openings through the casing and into the formation so that the fluids can enter the wellbore. The older style of perforator carries several bullets, which shoot holes in the casing and penetrate the formation as well. Today, perforation contractors nearly always use guns, jet perforators, that carry shaped charges (special explosive charges). The shaped charges work like the bullets in old-style perforators.

Perforating Guns

The perforating gun is a long cylinder that carries several bullets or shaped charges surrounded by a metal liner (fig. 2.3). The gun can be lowered into the hole in four ways: (1) through the casing on a conductor line, (2) on the end of the production tubing string, (3) through the tubing on the end of coiled tubing, or (4) through the tubing on a conductor line.

Manufacturers offer a variety of perforating guns. The choice depends basically on the diameter and length of the perforation needed and whether the gun will be lowered inside the casing or the tubing. The bigger the perforations need to be, the stronger the jets or the larger the bullets must be to make them. Stronger jets or larger bullets require larger charges and larger guns to hold the charges.

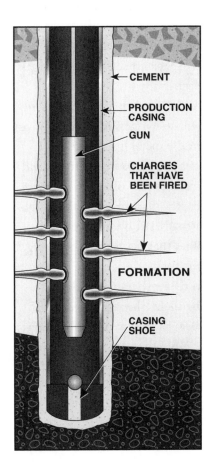

Figure 2.3. A jet perforating gun creates holes, or perforations, in the casing and into the surrounding formation.

Larger perforators are usually retrievable. In other words, the crew retrieves them after they fire the charges. Smaller perforators are partially or completely destroyed when the charges fire.

Where bullet perforators use bullets like an ordinary gun, jet perforators use shaped-charge explosives (fig. 2.4). Each shaped charge consists of an explosive material inside a cone-shaped charge case with a detonator on the back. A detonating cord runs to the surface where a perforating specialist sets off the charges electrically.

When a charge explodes, it generates a powerful shock wave on the metal liner. The liner breaks up into fine particles and becomes part of a high-energy jet stream, somewhat like a high-pressure stream of water from a hose, that blasts into the casing, cement, and rock to make a hole in them. Rather than destroying them, the stream pushes them aside as it moves through at more than 20,000 miles per hour (32,200 kilometres per hour). It may reach as far as 2 feet (.6 metres) before running out of energy.

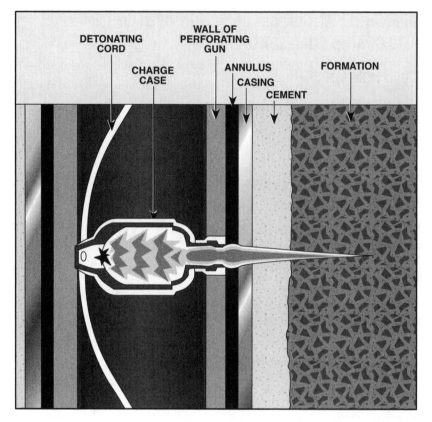

Figure 2.4. A shaped charge blasts a high-energy jet stream through the casing, the cement, and into the formation.

Perforating Procedures

After choosing the gun and charges, the perforating specialist assembles one or more guns and brings the assembly to the well. Sometimes the crew runs salt water into the well to displace the drilling mud and clean the hole of debris that might plug perforations. Then crew members lower the gun assembly to the correct depth and fire it.

To determine the exact position of the gun in relation to the formation outside the casing, the gun may have a *collar locator*.

One type of collar locator has arms that scrape against the walls of the casing. When the gun comes to a *casing collar,* or a coupling between two joints, the arms spring out into the gap between the joints. Since crew members have recorded the length of each joint, they can calculate the depth of the gun.

Sonic locators and magnetic locators find each casing coupling by locating the extra thickness of metal. Another type has a small video camera that shows the inside of the casing.

Perforated Liner Completion

Sometimes, instead of running production casing, the crew runs a liner below the intermediate casing. A *liner* is casing that hangs from the bottom of the intermediate casing instead of reaching all the way to the surface (fig. 2.5). It is cemented in, like casing, and is perforated in the same way as casing.

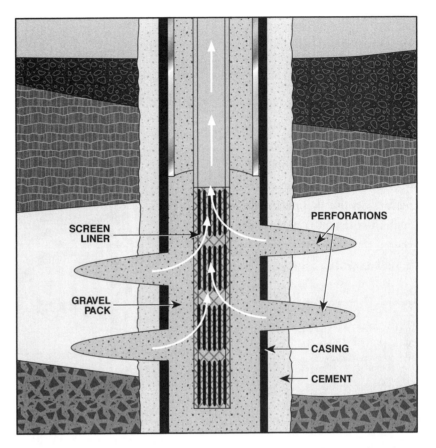

Figure 2.6. A wire-wrapped screen, or screen liner, is often combined with a gravel pack inside perforated casing.

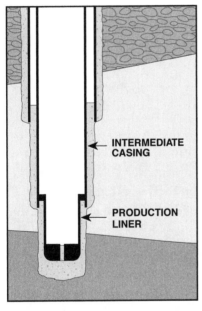

Figure 2.5. A production liner is run inside a previously run string of casing.

Wire-Wrapped Screen Completion

Some reservoirs produce not only oil and gas, but also sand. A formation produces sand when individual grains making up the reservoir rock are unconsolidated. In other words, rock grains do not adhere to each other. Sand can flow into the well along with the fluids and can clog it enough to reduce or stop production. Sand also damages the downhole equipment.

In reservoirs with sand, then, a completion sometimes includes a wire-wrapped screen, or screen liner, plus a gravel pack to keep sand out (fig. 2.6). The combination of a wire-wrapped screen and a gravel pack filters sand from the produced fluids. the screen and into the tubing (fig. 2.10D).

Wire-wrapped screen is a relatively short length of pipe with holes or slots in its sides and a specially shaped wire wrapped around it. The pipe with holes in it is called a *slotted liner*, and it is not the same thing as the liner described above that substitutes for casing in the hole (fig. 2.7). A slotted liner is just a pipe, the same diameter as the tubing, that attaches to the end of the last tubing joint.

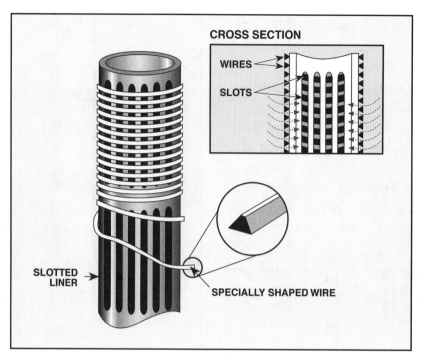

Figure 2.8. Specially shaped wire wraps around the slotted liner.

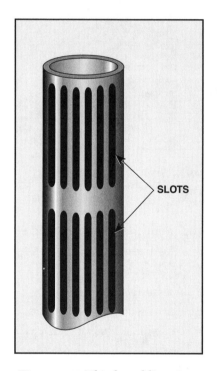

Figure 2.7. The slotted liner is a pipe with holes in it.

Wire that wraps around the liner has a cross section that looks like a keystone—a pyramid with its top cut off. The keystone shape creates a small opening that allows oil to flow through it, but keeps sand out (fig. 2.8).

Usually screen liners are used with a gravel pack. A *gravel pack* is made up of fine gravel—actually coarse sand—which filters out the finer sand in the formation. Figure 2.9 shows one way to place the gravel pack.

First, crew members circulate a fluid into the hole to wash out sand at the bottom (fig. 2.9A). Then they pump gravel down the tubing in a viscous (thick) fluid (fig. 2.9B). Next they run in the screen liner (fig. 2.9C). Finally, they close a back-pressure valve on the bottom of the tubing which allows reservoir fluids to flow through the screen and into the tubing (fig. 2.9D).

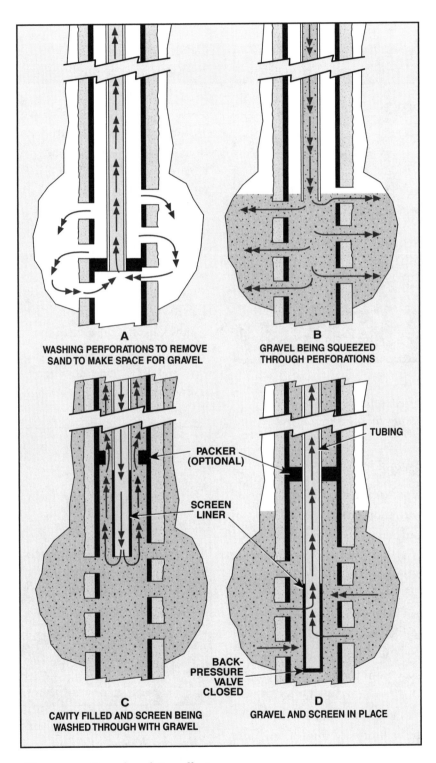

Figure 2.9. Gravel pack installation

TUBING AND PACKERS

Tubing

Tubing is the final string of pipe run into a well. Unlike casing, it is a removable pipe string. Well fluids flow from the reservoir to the surface through tubing. Tubing is smaller in diameter than casing—the outside diameter ranges from about 1 to 4½ inches (about 25 to 114 millimetres).

As they do with casing, crew members screw together individual joints of tubing, each of which is about 30 feet (9 metres) long, with couplings to make up a string. The string usually hangs from the *tubing head*, a special fitting at the surface.

Rig operators nearly always run tubing in a well because oil and gas produce better through small-diameter tubing than through large-diameter casing, the way a river flows faster through a narrow channel than through a wide bed. Also, servicing crews can remove tubing if it becomes plugged or damaged. They cannot easily remove casing because it is cemented in the well.

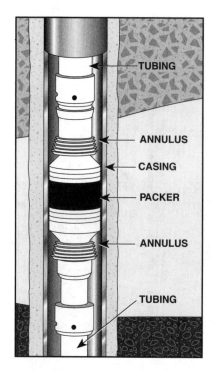

Figure 2.10. *A packer goes around tubing and seals the casing-tubing annulus.*

Packers

A *packer* is a cylinder that screws onto tubing near the bottom and acts as a seal in the *annulus*, or cylindrical hole, between the tubing and the casing (fig. 2.10).

A packer provides a secure seal between everything above and below where it is set, and keeps well fluids and pressure away from the casing above it. One reason to isolate the casing is to keep sand and sediment in the produced fluids from eroding it, in the same way

sandblasting etches glass. Sulfur and other naturally occurring chemicals in reservoir fluids are another enemy of casing and cause the metal to corrode. Tubing can erode and corrode, too, but it can be pulled and repaired or replaced, since it is not cemented in the hole. Also, corrosion-resistant tubing is cheaper than corrosion-resistant casing because tubing is smaller.

The sealing element of a packer, the *packing element*, is a dense synthetic rubber ring that expands against the side of the casing (fig. 2.11). A packer may have one packing element or several, separated by metal rings.

Figure 2.11. *The sealing element of a packer is made of dense synthetic rubber.*

If the packer moves up or down while the packing elements are expanded, they will rub off against the casing, like an automobile tire against a curb. To prevent this, packers have slips to hold them in place.

A slip is a serrated piece of metal that grips the side of the casing (fig. 2.12). Upward-pointing slips prevent upward movement, and downward-pointing slips prevent downward movement. While the crew is positioning

the packer, the slips are folded out of the way. A setting mechanism moves them outward when the packer is in the desired location.

Most packers have a circulation valve that allows fluids to pass through them. Although a packer usually seals fluids off from the annulus, sometimes a crew opens the circulation valve and uses a circulating fluid to set or retrieve the packer.

Retrievable Packers

A *retrievable packer,* as the name suggests, can be pulled out of the well when it fails, to be repaired or replaced. Usually it is run into the well on the end of drill pipe or tubing and requires movement to set it, often a combination of rotating the tubing and setting the weight of the tubing onto the packer. To release it, the crew just pulls it up or pulls and rotates it the direction opposite setting rotation. Its retrievability also allows the crew to move it a few feet and reset it. Because of its intricate setting and release mechanisms, it is larger, more expensive, and not as strong as a permanent packer.

SLIPS

Figure 2.12. The slips grip casing to hold the packer in place.

Permanent Packers

Today, many rig operators use *permanent*, or *drillable packers*. The metal parts of a permanent packer are cast iron or brass, relatively soft metals. When a crew needs to replace the packer, crew members drill it out with a *packer mill*, a bit that grinds up the metal.

The crew sets a permanent packer by running it in on a conductor line instead of tubing. Unlike a retrievable packer, a permanent packer is set electrically. A small explosive charge sets the slips and expands the packing elements. A permanent packer is faster and cheaper to install, and can even be run in at the same time as the perforating gun.

After setting the packer, a crew sometimes pumps *packer fluid* into the annulus to hold back the pressure from the formation (see fig. 2.10). Packer fluid is usually salt water, or brine.

Tubingless Completion

Although the final string of pipe in most wells is the tubing, some small-diameter wells that use small-diameter casing may be completed without tubing; these are *tubingless completions*. Small reservoirs that produce mostly natural gas often have tubingless completions.

Multiple Completion

A crew uses a multiple completion when one wellbore passes through two or more zones with oil and gas in them. Usually, a separate tubing string and packer are run in for each producing zone. For example, a triple completion has three tubing strings and three packers, and each zone produces independently of the others.

THE WELLHEAD

The *wellhead* includes all equipment on the surface that supports various pipe strings, seals off the well, and controls the paths and flow rates of reservoir fluids. All wellheads have at least one casinghead and casing hanger, usually a tubing head and tubing hanger, and a Christmas tree (fig. 2.13).

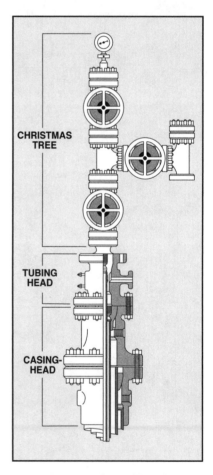

Figure 2.13. The wellhead includes the equipment that supports the pipe strings, seals off the well, and controls the paths and flow rates of reservoir fluids.

Casinghead

A *casinghead* consists of several parts attached to the top of a string of casing after each string has been run in and cemented. If a well has only surface casing and production casing, the surface casing screws into a threaded coupling welded onto the casinghead and the production casing hangs from a casing hanger (fig. 2.14). A *casing hanger* is a set of slips that grip and support a casing string. Metal and rubber seals fit over the slips to seal the casinghead and prevent fluids from moving within the wellhead or escaping to the atmosphere. The casinghead also has a place for screwing in a pressure gauge to warn of leaks.

When completion requires an intermediate casing string, a second casinghead stacks on top of the first one (fig. 2.15). In this case, the intermediate casing hangs from a hanger in the bottom casinghead, and the production casing from a hanger in the top casinghead.

Figure 2.15. This example shows three casing strings hanging from two casingheads. The first casinghead is screwed onto the surface casing. The other casing strings are suspended from casing hangers.

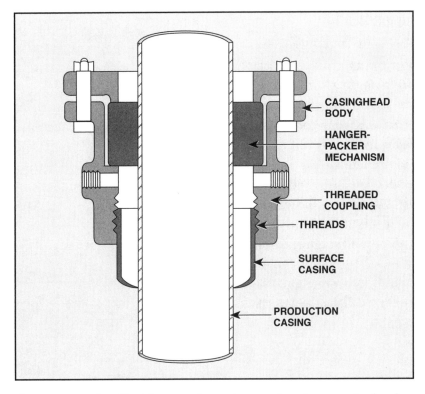

Figure 2.14. *A well with two casing strings needs only one casinghead.*

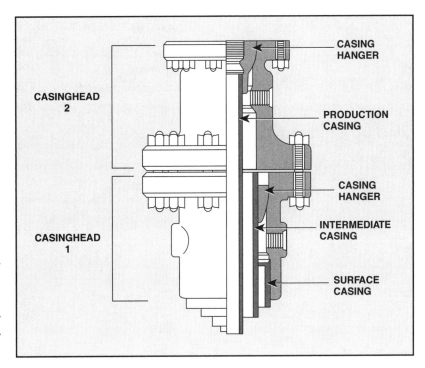

Tubing Head

The *tubing head* often stacks onto the uppermost casinghead (fig. 2.16). In a low-pressure well that has no casinghead, it may be attached to the production casing itself. Its *tubing hanger* seals the annulus between the production casing and the tubing and supports the weight of the tubing string. Like the casingheads, it has outlets to allow access to the annulus for gauging pressure or connecting valves and fittings to control the flow of fluids.

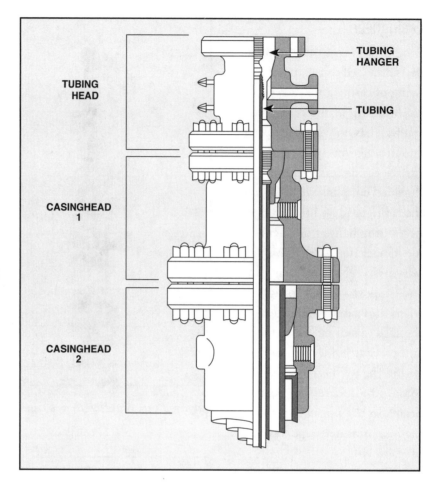

Figure 2.16. The tubing string hangs from a tubing head, which can be stacked on top of the casinghead. Notice that individual strings of casing and tubing are isolated from each other so that no pressure or fluids from one string can get into another.

Figure 2.17. The Christmas tree is mounted on top of the tubing head.

Christmas Tree

High-pressure wells usually have a group of valves and fittings called a *Christmas tree* (fig. 2.17), a name derived from its tree-like appearance. They regulate, measure, and direct the flow of fluids from the well. Low-pressure wells may also have Christmas trees, but these trees are less complex than high-pressure ones.

Pressure gauges on a Christmas tree measure pressure both in the casing and in the tubing and can warn of leaks.

Rig operators have more control over the well if they know the pressures under various operating conditions.

Valves on a tree work like those on an outdoor water faucet. They can be opened and closed to control the flow of fluids from the well. The main valve is the *master valve,* just above the tubing head. Opening the master valve allows the fluids to flow to the flow line; closing it shuts off the flow of reservoir fluids entirely.

Another important part of a Christmas tree is the choke. It is a restriction in the line. The choke restricts the flow of fluids as they leave the tree. The size of the choke's opening may be fixed or adjustable. A fixed choke must be replaced to change the well's producing rate. The opening of an adjustable choke changes size when a worker turns a control handle.

STARTING THE FLOW

As a well is drilled, pressure in the producing zone is offset by the pressure of the drilling fluid (drilling mud) in the hole. The drilling crew leaves this heavy mud inside the casing after drilling is complete so that its pressure will continue to offset formation pressure after the casing is perforated. The completion crew usually runs production tubing into the well while the drilling fluid is still in place.

Next, they wash in the well; that is, they displace the mud in the tubing by pumping salt water into it (fig. 2.18) and setting the packer. This results in a column of water holding back the formation pressure. Water exerts less pressure than drilling mud, so there may be enough pressure in the formation to overcome it and start the oil or gas flowing through the perforations into the well and up the tubing. When the reservoir oil or gas pushes all the salt water up out of the tubing, pressure at the wellhead will be at its highest. Generally, gas or oil will follow soon after all the water is out. Until production is pure, the mixture of oil, gas, and water goes into a tank, from which the water will later be disposed.

If reservoir pressure is not high enough to overcome saltwater pressure and push hydrocarbons out of the well, swabbing may be necessary to unload the well. *Unloading* a well means removing some of the brine pumped in when the well was washed in. Less brine means less pressure for the formation pressure to overcome, so often the well will begin flowing after it is swabbed. Chapter 7 includes a more detailed description of how swabbing works.

Another means of starting production flow is to force high-pressure gas into the tubing before setting the packer (fig. 2.19). Gas pushes the brine in the tubing down, out into the annulus between the tubing and the casing, then up. The packer is then set, leaving only a short column of fluid in the tubing holding pressure on the formation. The well will often start flowing immediately.

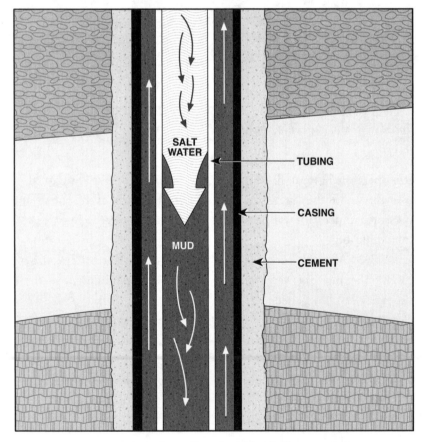

Figure 2.18. Washing in the well replaces the drilling mud that was holding back formation pressure with salt water.

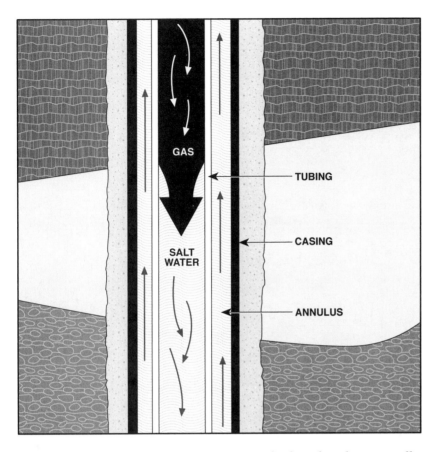

Figure 2.19. Injecting a high-pressure gas to displace the salt water will often start the well flowing.

COMPLETING GAS WELLS

Gas wells are generally completed in the same way as oil-producing wells except that they never require artificial lift—natural gas always flows without help. Most gas wells can be washed into production. Pressure at the surface is usually higher in a gas well than in an oil producer, but if the pressure is low, swabbing off water in the tubing may be necessary.

Sometimes a well does not flow at a fast enough rate, given the known amount of hydrocarbons in the reservoir, after these completion operations. The company representative may then decide to stimulate the reservoir to make the well produce at an acceptable rate. *Stimulation* is one of several processes that enlarge or create channels in the reservoir rock so that oil and gas can move through it and into the well. Chapter 10 describes how stimulation works.

If a well does not flow on its own after washing in, swabbing, and stimulation, an artificial means of lifting oil to the surface is needed, usually some sort of pump. The next chapter details various types of artificial lift.

When hydrocarbons do flow out of the well, they go through a pipe called the *flow line* to a storage tank and gas separators. From there separate gas and oil pipelines transport them, sometimes many miles or kilometres for refining and sale.

3

ARTIFICIAL LIFT

After tubing has been run in, the packer set, and the well perforated, hydrocarbons usually flow to the surface immediately or after a crew swabs the well. When pressure from natural reservoir drive falls to the point where a well cannot produce on its own, however, an artificial method of lifting the hydrocarbons is necessary. Artificial lift is most commonly provided by some sort of pump or a method that involves injecting gas into the well.

BEAM PUMPING

By far the most common method of artificially pumping oil from the formation to the surface in land-based wells is beam pumping. A *beam pumping unit* sits on the surface (fig. 3.1). It sends an up-and-down motion, called *reciprocating action,* to a string of rods called sucker rods. *Sucker rods* are solid, high-strength steel (or sometimes fiberglass) rods connected together. The top of a sucker rod string is attached to the front of a pumping unit, usually to a walking beam, and hangs down inside the tubing. At the end of the string, near the bottom of the well, is a sucker rod pump. The walking beam's reciprocating action moves the rod string up and down to operate the pump.

Figure 3.1. The beam pumping unit is a familiar sight in oil country.

33

Beam Pumping Units

Of the four basic types of beam pumping units, three include a walking beam, which seesaws to provide the reciprocating movement. The fourth reciprocates by winding a cable on and off a rotating drum. The job of all four types is to change the circular movement of an engine or motor to a reciprocating motion to run the pump.

In a conventional beam pumping unit, the prime mover (an electric motor or a gas engine) drives a set of gears called a speed reducer by means of belts (fig. 3.2). The speed reducer changes the fast rotating motion of the prime mover to the slow motion needed for pumping. For example, an engine may run at a speed of 600 revolutions per minute, but the pumping unit may need to operate at 20 strokes per minute. The gears in the speed reducer make it possible to slow to the correct pumping speed.

A slow-moving crankshaft, or bull shaft, extends from either side of the speed reducer. Each end of the crankshaft is attached to a steel member called a crank or crank arm. A set of weights on each crank counterbalances the weight of the sucker rod string.

Figure 3.2. Gears transfer power from the prime mover and slow the fast rotating motion of the prime mover to a more correct pumping speed.

Two metal arms called pitmans connect the cranks to the walking beam. They convert the circular motion of the cranks into a reciprocating motion of the walking beam. On the front of the walking beam is a steel piece called the horsehead. A hanger made from a crosspiece and two cables, the bridle, extends down from the horsehead. The first sucker rod hangs from the bridle.

Cable-operated pumping units that spool a cable on and off a drum to transfer reciprocating motion to the sucker rods are rare in the United States. They are used mainly on offshore rigs due to space limitations.

Sucker Rods

The first rod that hangs from the bridle is the polished rod (see fig. 3.1). The polished rod, which is usually very bright and shiny, moves up and down inside a stuffing box. The stuffing box has flexible packing material inside it to form a pressure-tight seal around the polished rod and the inside of the tubing. The packing keeps liquids or gases from leaking out around the polished rod.

A steel sucker rod (also called a joint) is usually 25 feet (7.6 metres) long; a fiberglass rod is 37.5 feet (11.4 metres) long. Each rod has a threaded male connection on both ends called a pin (fig. 3.3). Since rods meet pin to pin, a coupling connects them (fig. 3.4). A flat area next to the pin and a flat area on the coupling provides a place for a wrench to grip the rod and coupling when screwing or unscrewing a coupling.

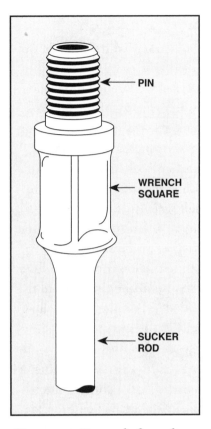

Figure 3.3. One end of a sucker rod shows the flat section where a wrench can grip it and one of the threaded pins on each end.

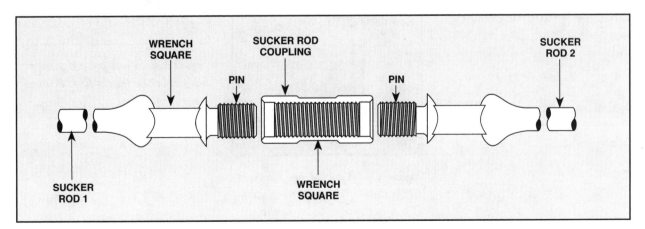

Figure 3.4. A sucker rod coupling connects the rod pins to make up a string of sucker rods.

Sucker Rod Pumps

The sucker rod pump at the bottom of the rod string lifts oil to the surface through production tubing (fig. 3.5). Its main parts are the barrel, plunger, traveling valve, standing valve, and gas anchor. Although manufacturers sell dozens of pump designs to suit specific downhole conditions, they all work like a piston moving inside a cylinder.

The plunger corresponds to the piston, and the barrel to the cylinder. The plunger is hollow and attaches to the end of the sucker rod string. As the pumping unit moves the rod string up and down, the plunger moves, or strokes, up and down inside the barrel. The plunger may be either soft-packed or metallic. A soft-packed plunger has rubber and fabric cups or rings on a metal mandrel that form a seal against the barrel (fig. 3.6). A metallic plunger is a precision-fitted tube coated with a hard metal alloy that fits accurately inside the barrel.

The standing valve and the traveling valve are ball valves. They open and close by means of a ball seated over an opening.

Usually a standing valve is near the bottom of the barrel, and a traveling valve is above it, in the bottom of the plunger (see fig. 3.5). When one of these valves is open, the other is closed.

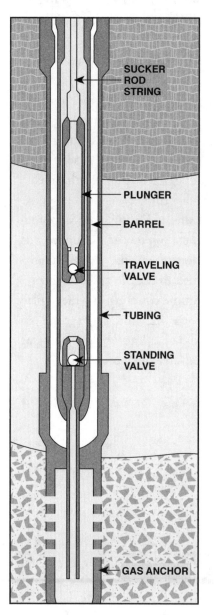

Figure 3.5. A sucker rod pump at the bottom of the sucker rod string lifts the reservoir fluids to the surface.

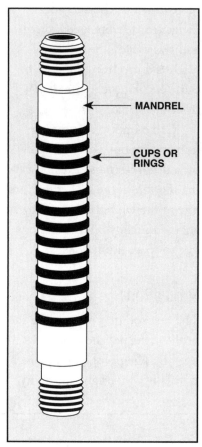

Figure 3.6. A soft-packed plunger has rubber or fabric rings around a metal mandrel.

When a beam unit pulls the sucker rod string and plunger up (fig. 3.7A), the fluid below the pump pushes the ball in the standing valve off its seat to open the valve. At the same time, the weight of the fluid already in the plunger above the traveling valve moves its ball against the seat to close the valve. The well fluids enter the barrel through the open standing valve during the upstroke and fill it up.

On the downstroke of the plunger (fig. 3.7B), the traveling valve opens and the standing valve closes, forcing fluid up and out of the barrel through the hollow plunger. The fluid leaves the plunger and goes into the tubing above the pump. Repeating this process forces the fluid up to the surface through the tubing.

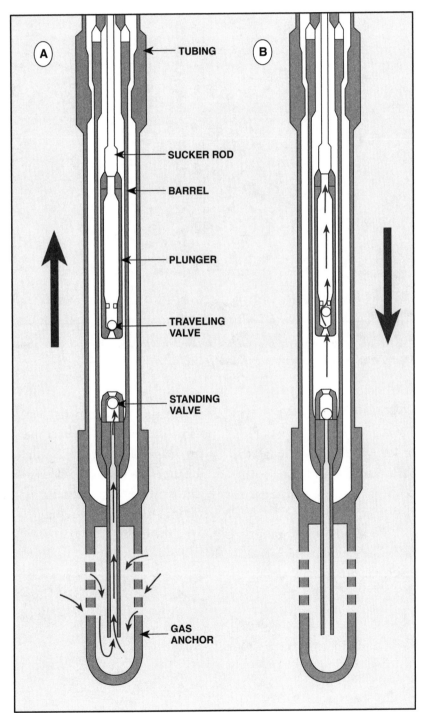

Figure 3.7. (A) The plunger is moving up, which closes the traveling valve and opens the standing valve. Well fluids (arrows) are drawn through the gas anchor into the center of the pump. (B) The plunger is now moving down, which opens the traveling valve and closes the standing valve. Well fluids travel up through the plunger and out the top of the pump.

The gas anchor is a hollow cylinder with perforations that is attached to the bottom of the pump. Its purpose is to help prevent gas lock. Gas lock happens when dissolved gas in the well fluids is released from solution on the upstroke of the plunger. If the pressure of gas is high enough, the gas pushes down on the standing valve, locking it shut. No more fluids can enter the barrel, so the pump stops pumping. A gas anchor (fig. 3.8) works on the principle that gas, being lighter than oil, rises. As well fluids enter the anchor, gas breaks out of solution and passes out of the anchor through holes in the outer tubing. The remaining fluids enter the pump through inner tubing at the bottom of the anchor. All or most of the gas escapes before it can lock up the pump.

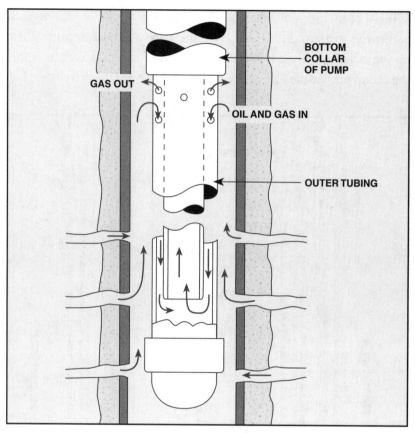

Figure 3.8. A gas anchor is attached to the bottom of a sucker rod pump. It prevents gas in the reservoir fluids from locking the pump.

Types of Sucker Rod Pumps

There are two main types of sucker rod pumps, although the basic design and working parts described above are the same on all of them.

The insert (or rod) pump fits inside a barrel, which goes inside the production tubing.

A crew runs the pump and barrel on the end of the sucker rod string and can remove it by pulling the rods (fig. 3.9A). This allows them to make repairs without removing the tubing from the well.

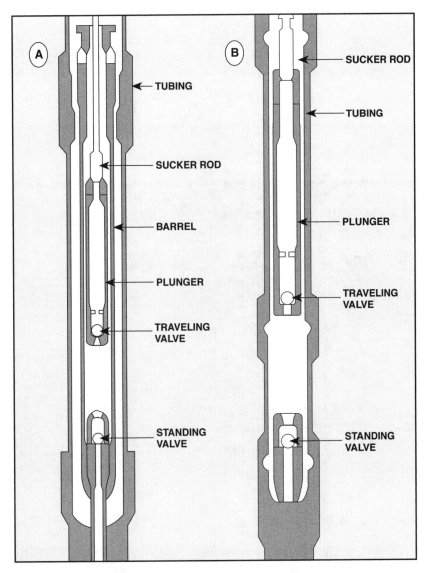

In a tubing pump, on the other hand, the barrel is like the last joint on the tubing string (fig. 3.9B). The plunger and the traveling valve are run in with the sucker rods. The standing valve can be either fixed (part of the tubing string) or retrievable (removable with the rod string).

Although a tubing pump is more difficult to repair than an insert pump (the crew has to pull the tubing to get to it), it has one advantage. It has more inside volume than an insert pump because the barrel is the same diameter as the tubing, and therefore it pumps more fluid with each stroke.

Figure 3.9. (A) An insert pump fits inside the production tubing. (B) A tubing pump's barrel is the last joint on the tubing string.

ELECTRIC SUBMERSIBLE PUMPS

In many fields, older wells that have been using beam pumping units gradually begin producing much more water than oil. In order to recover enough oil to be profitable, tremendous volumes of fluid have to be lifted from the well. For this reason, electric submersible pumps (fig. 3.10) have become popular because the rig operator can stack as many pumps as needed in the well. Both the pump motors and the pumps are downhole, submerged in the well fluid, on the end of the tubing string. A special heavy-duty armored cable supplies electricity to them. The main disadvantage of submersible pumps is that they are sensitive to sand and gas.

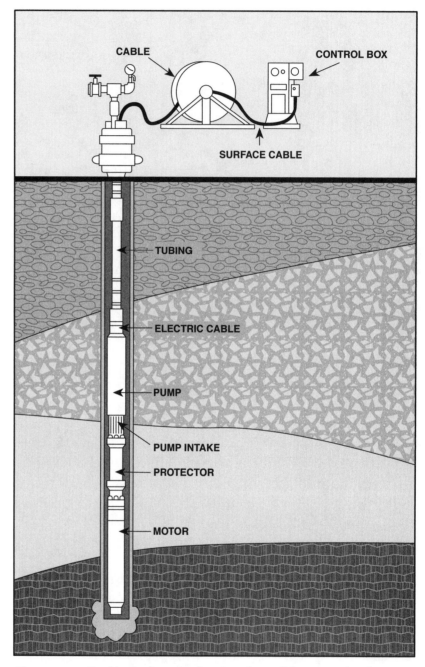

Figure 3.10. In this single-stage electric submersible pump, the electric motor turns impellers in the pump. The protector insulates the motor from the pump.

Pump

Essentially, a submersible pump consists of a long centrifugal pump that has several impellers one above the other on a central shaft (fig. 3.11). An impeller is a bladed device that moves fluids when it turns, like a fan moves air when it turns. The shaft is connected to a long electric motor. When the motor is turned on, the impellers spin. Spinning impellers move the reservoir fluids that surround them out and up the tubing by centrifugal force. Centrifugal force is what pushes a child on a merry-go-round outward.

Several pumps stack on top of one another to make up a pump stage, or multistage pump. A single well can have hundreds of stages, but usually has 15 to 20.

Other Downhole Equipment

An electric motor is at the bottom of the pump assembly. A steel housing filled with oil encloses the motor. Oil lubricates a motor's moving parts and transmits heat away from it to the well fluids, so well fluids cool the motor as they flow around it. Because the diameter of casing limits the size and power of the motor, rig operators often stack several motors to get the horsepower they need.

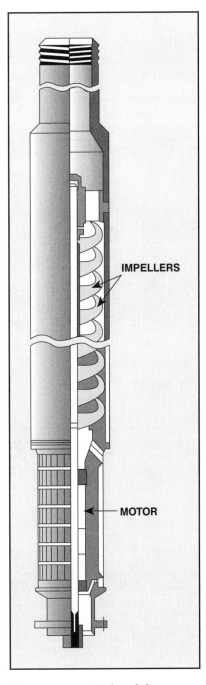

Figure 3.11. Blades of the impellers inside a pump force well fluids out and up by centrifugal force when the impellers spin.

A protector between the pump and the motor seals well fluids away from the motor and buffers the pump from the movement of the motor. A gas separator connects the motor to the protector. Like the gas anchor on a rod pump, it keeps gas out of the pump (see fig. 3.10).

HYDRAULIC PUMPING

A third pumping system is hydraulic pumping. Hydraulic pumping is similar to beam pumping in that an engine on the surface powers a pump in the hole. The engine uses hydraulic energy, or the energy of a flowing liquid, however, to make the pump work instead of sucker rods. Because a hydraulic pump does not use sucker rods, it is less complicated to service than a mechanical system, and it can work in deeper wells than sucker rod pumps. Erosion wears out the pump relatively quickly, though.

A hydraulic system actually has two pumps: an ordinary electric or engine-driven pump on the surface to force a liquid, called the power fluid, down the hole, and a hydraulic pump at the bottom of the well that the power fluid runs.

Surface Equipment

Power fluid is usually just crude oil produced from a well. Because it may have sand or other abrasives in it which could damage the hydraulic pump, it passes continuously through conditioning equipment on the surface to clean it. Surface installations may be open systems or closed systems.

An open system (fig. 3.12) circulates fluids that the pump lifts from the reservoir itself as the power fluid. The produced crude oil moving up from the well flows through a boot, which separates gas from liquid oil. Oil then flows into a settling tank, where any solids in it settle out. Part of the cleaned oil flows from the top of the settling tank to a surface pump powered by an electric motor or engine. The oil becomes the power fluid as the pump sends it back into the well through a special tubing string.

This tubing string is not the production tubing. It is a smaller-diameter string either inside the production tubing or next to it inside the casing. Figure 3.12 shows concentric tubing strings and parallel strings. In either case, the downhole hydraulic pump is inside the power fluid string.

When well fluid is too difficult to clean, well servicing contractors use a closed system. A closed system keeps the power fluid separate from produced oil and recirculates it through the hydraulic pump. The fluid in a closed system is usually oil but may be treated water.

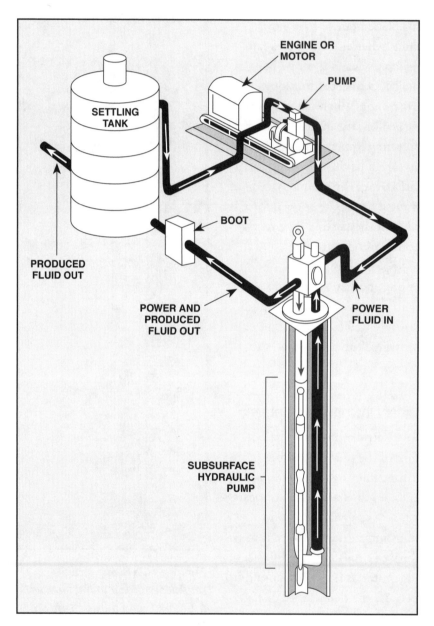

Figure 3.12.   An open hydraulic system has surface and downhole components.

Downhole Equipment

The hydraulic pump at the bottom has two pistons: an engine piston and a pump piston (fig. 3.13). Power fluid passes through ports in the wall of the pump and moves the engine piston up and down, which drives the pump piston. Valves in both sections open and close in rhythm with the piston strokes to pump the power fluid and reservoir fluids through the hydraulic pump and up to the surface, much as a sucker rod pump does.

Down the well, hydraulic pumping systems fall into one of two broad categories: (1) *conventional*, or *fixed pump*, installations, in which the subsurface pump is connected to the end of the power fluid tubing string; and (2) *free pump* installations, in which the subsurface pump moves freely inside power fluid tubing string. A free pump has an advantage in that the hydraulic force of power fluid lowers it into the well when flowing in one direction and pulls it up from the well when the direction of the flow is reversed. To retrieve a fixed pump, the service crew must pull the tubing. Most modern systems use free pump installations.

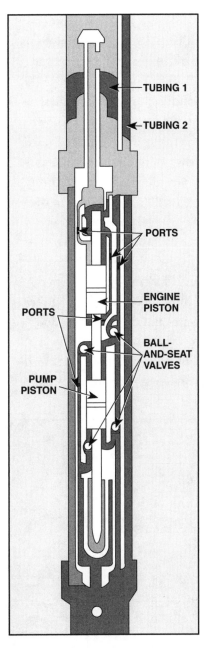

Figure 3.13. A downhole hydraulic pump consists of two pistons, ports to let in the power fluid, and valves.

Well servicing contractors can choose from several styles of pump installations within the broader categories of fixed and free pumps. These arrangements vary according to how the power oil returns to the surface, whether and how formation gas is vented, and how the produced fluids reach the surface.

GAS LIFT

The term "gas lift" covers a variety of methods by which gas is used to increase the production of a well or to restore production to a dead well. When a well flows on its own, it may be using a natural form of gas lift—dissolved-gas drive or gas-cap drive. Natural gas can also be injected into a well to lift the oil artificially on the same principle. The completion crew installs gas-lift valves on the production tubing. Valves allow gas to be forced into the annulus to pass into the tubing and into the liquid there.

To understand the principle of gas lift, recall that gas is lighter than oil and water. For example, 1 gallon (cubic metre) of water weighs a little over 8 pounds (119 kilograms), while 1 gallon (cubic metre) of natural gas weighs only a fraction of an ounce (kilogram). When natural gas enters liquid in the tubing, the gas makes this liquid column much lighter. Since the liquid column is lighter, it exerts less pressure on the bottom of the well. With pressure lower at the bottom, the pressure remaining in the reservoir becomes sufficient to push reservoir fluids to the surface through the tubing.

Figure 3.14 shows how gas-lift valves work. Before lifting begins, the tubing and casing are full of well liquids. All of the gas-lift valves are open. A compressor on the surface forces gas down the casing until it reaches valve 1. Since valve 1 is open, gas enters it and lifts liquids out of the tubing (fig. 3.14A). Valve 1 then closes. The gas moves down to valve 2, which is still open. The gas goes through the open valve and lifts more liquids from the tubing (fig. 3.14B). Valve 2 then closes and the gas moves down to valve 3, which is still open. The gas lifts all the liquids from the tubing and the well produces

(fig. 3.14C). The well produces because gas has reduced the pressure on the bottom of the well.

A production company may inject the gas continuously or intermittently. In a continuous system, one valve remains open and gas is injected at a constant rate. In an intermittent system, the valve opens and closes automatically according to the pressure in the annulus.

Gas lift is a practical method offshore, where space is limited and natural gas is usually in great supply.

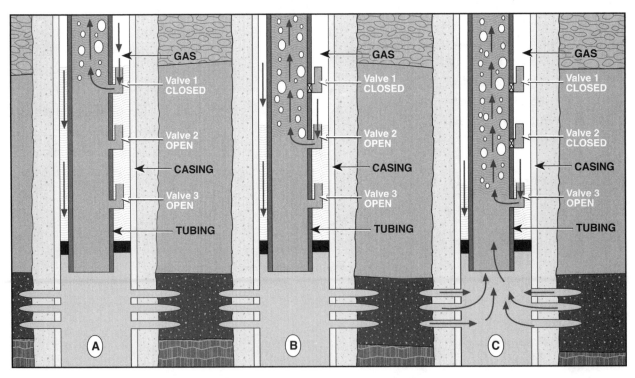

Figure 3.14. Gas lift valves are installed in the tubing at various depths. Gas enters the tubing through the valves and aerates the heavier fluids to lift them to the surface.

4
LOGGING AND TESTING A WELL

Logging and testing wells occur during drilling, completion, service, and workover. Logging and testing specialists use many types of instruments and techniques to reveal information about the condition and location of the reservoir, formation fluids, wellbore, circulation fluids, and equipment in the hole. This chapter is an overview of some of the main types of logs and tests.

A *log* is a permanent record of information about the formations a well has drilled through. There are many ways to log, or survey, a well. Some involve observations of the drilling conditions and rock, and others involve lowering a tool into the well that sends signals to an observer on the surface.

DRILL STEM TEST

The drilling crew runs a drill stem test (or DST) to test a formation it has just drilled into. The DST gives accurate data about a formation's pressure and the composition of the fluids in it. A DST tool is run in on the end of the drill stem (fig. 4.1). It has one or two packers that isolate the zone to be tested. A perforated pipe between the two packers, or between one packer and the bottom of the hole, allows formation fluids to flow in. A pressure recorder inside the tool above the packer and another below the perforated pipe chart the pressure. When the pressure testing is finished, valves in the DST tool close to trap a fluid sample, the packer is released, and the tool is retrieved.

Analyzing the DST reveals reservoir pressure, average permeability, the presence and location of permeability changes, formation damage, production potential, and pressure depletion rate.

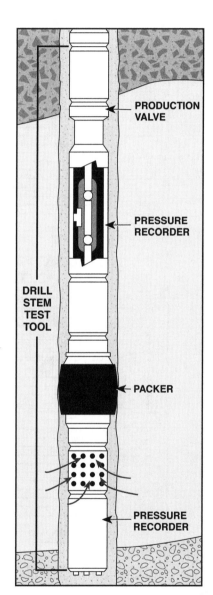

Figure 4.1. A drill stem test tool records pressure and samples the formation fluid.

45

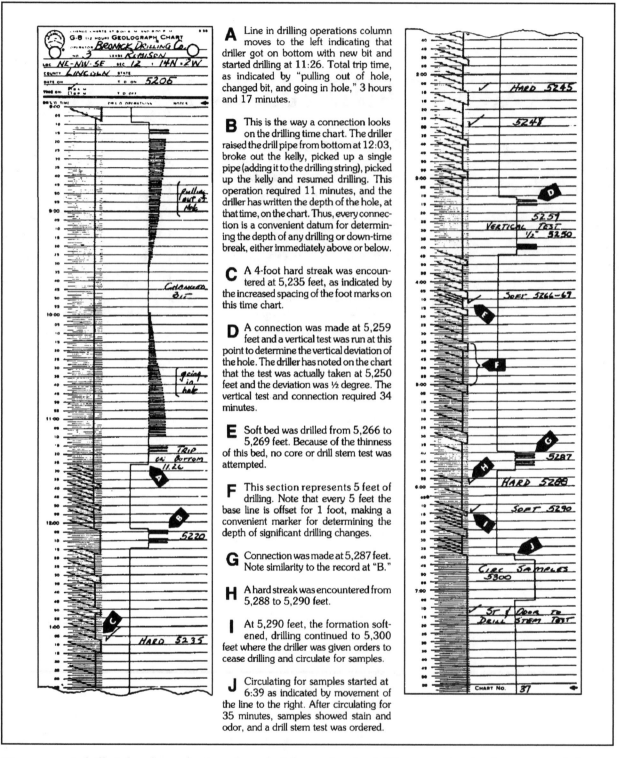

A Line in drilling operations column moves to the left indicating that driller got on bottom with new bit and started drilling at 11:26. Total trip time, as indicated by "pulling out of hole, changed bit, and going in hole," 3 hours and 17 minutes.

B This is the way a connection looks on the drilling time chart. The driller raised the drill pipe from bottom at 12:03, broke out the kelly, picked up a single pipe (adding it to the drilling string), picked up the kelly and resumed drilling. This operation required 11 minutes, and the driller has written the depth of the hole, at that time, on the chart. Thus, every connection is a convenient datum for determining the depth of any drilling or down-time break, either immediately above or below.

C A 4-foot hard streak was encountered at 5,235 feet, as indicated by the increased spacing of the foot marks on this time chart.

D A connection was made at 5,259 feet and a vertical test was run at this point to determine the vertical deviation of the hole. The driller has noted on the chart that the test was actually taken at 5,250 feet and the deviation was ½ degree. The vertical test and connection required 34 minutes.

E Soft bed was drilled from 5,266 to 5,269 feet. Because of the thinness of this bed, no core or drill stem test was attempted.

F This section represents 5 feet of drilling. Note that every 5 feet the base line is offset for 1 foot, making a convenient marker for determining the depth of significant drilling changes.

G Connection was made at 5,287 feet. Note similarity to the record at "B."

H A hard streak was encountered from 5,288 to 5,290 feet.

I At 5,290 feet, the formation softened, drilling continued to 5,300 feet where the driller was given orders to cease drilling and circulate for samples.

J Circulating for samples started at 6:39 as indicated by movement of the line to the right. After circulating for 35 minutes, samples showed stain and odor, and a drill stem test was ordered.

Figure 4.2. A driller's log charts the time along the left margin, the drilling operation in the center, and the driller's notes on the right. Each slanted line drawn on the left represents one foot drilled, so the farther apart they are, the slower the drilling.

MECHANICAL LOGS

Mechanical logs include several ways of recording the properties of the underground formation by direct observations at the surface.

The simplest and first log of a well is the driller's log (fig. 4.2). In this log, drillers write down the types of rock they find at what depth, the fluids in them, and anything else of interest about the drilling operation. The driller's log is particularly useful when drilling a second well in an area. The driller keeps track of how long it took to drill through a particular layer of rock, for example, which helps predict how long drilling in later wells may take.

Another direct method of finding out what types of rock a well has penetrated is to drill a core (fig. 4.3). A *core* is a cylinder of rock a few inches (or millimetres) in diameter and 25 to 60 feet (7.6 to 18.3 metres) long drilled with a special coring bit that is hollow in the center. A laboratory analysis can reveal many characteristics of the rock in a core and how much oil it is likely to contain.

Geologists also examine cuttings brought up with the drilling mud and record their observations in a mud log.

WIRELINE LOGS

Oilfield workers also have several methods of indirectly getting information about formations and equipment down the hole. These wireline logs record information provided by a tool run into the well on wireline or conductor line. Wireline and conductor line are the same type of metal line, except that a conductor line conducts electricity to the tool on the end of it and a wireline does not. Oilfield workers sometimes call any job that uses a wireline to lower a tool into the well a "wireline service" or operation and these tools "wireline tools." Wireline services include jobs that use conductor line because, in the oil patch, a conductor line is often referred to as a wireline.

Wireline logging often involves complex calculations and interpretation of the information a tool relays to the surface. The logging specialist uses a computer to compare, or correlate, data from various surveys, to print it out in the form of charts or graphs, to keep track of the depth of the logging tool, and to warn of malfunctions.

Figure 4.3. A core is a cylinder of rock a few inches in diameter drilled from deep in the earth.

Acoustic Logs

An *acoustic*, or *sonic log* is a record of sound waves sent through the rock (fig. 4.4). How fast sound travels through a rock depends on its composition and how much fluid it contains.

As rock becomes more porous, the waves travel faster. The tool that transmits and receives a constant ticking sound for this log is an acoustic sonde (pronounced "sond") (fig. 4.5).

An acoustic sonde works only in a hole that has liquid in it. The liquid provides a link to transmit the sound waves from the tool to the formation, like a lake transmits a wave from a moving boat.

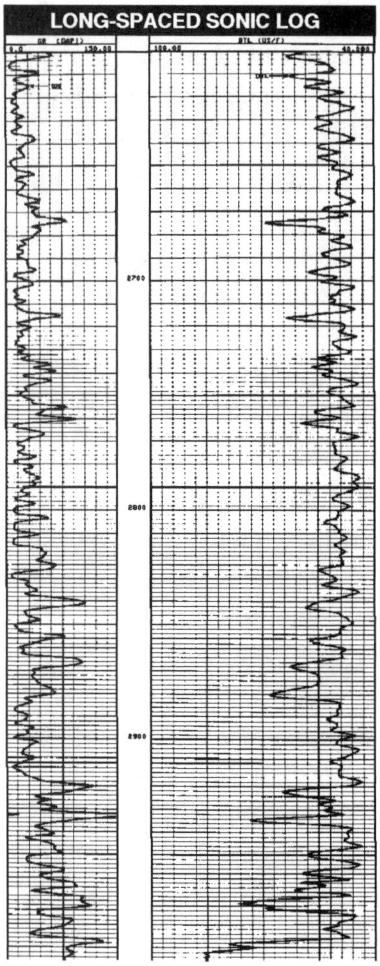

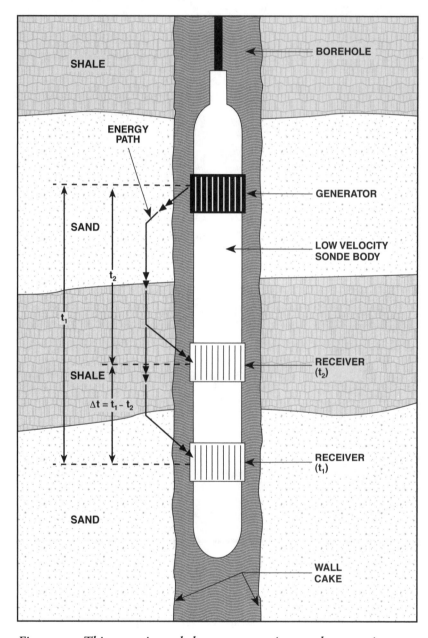

Figure 4.4. An acoustic (sonic) log is a curved line that moves horizontally to show the speed of sound waves and vertically to show depth.

Figure 4.5. This acoustic sonde has one transmitter and two receivers.

A *cement bond survey* uses an acoustic sonde to determine the quality and location of the cement behind the casing. Casing that has a good bond with the cement transmits the acoustic signal quickly; poorly bonded casing transmits it slowly. A workover crew fills any channels or voids that the survey locates.

Electric Logs

Two types of electric logs record electrical currents. One type, a *spontaneous potential (SP) log*, records weak electrical currents that flow naturally in the rock next to the wellbore (natural electricity). It shows the boundaries and thickness of each layer of rock.

In another type, a sonde sends an electrical signal through the formation and relays it back to a receiver at the surface (induced electricity). The surface detector may measure either the formation's resistance to the current or how well it conducts the current.

A *resistivity log* records resistance, and an *induction log* records conductivity. For example, salt water conducts electricity better than oil, so its resistance is lower. Figure 4.6 shows an SP log on the left and a resistivity log on the right.

These types of electric logs reveal the formation's porosity and permeability, hydrocarbon content, how much water is mixed in with the hydrocarbons, and whether drilling mud has damaged the formation.

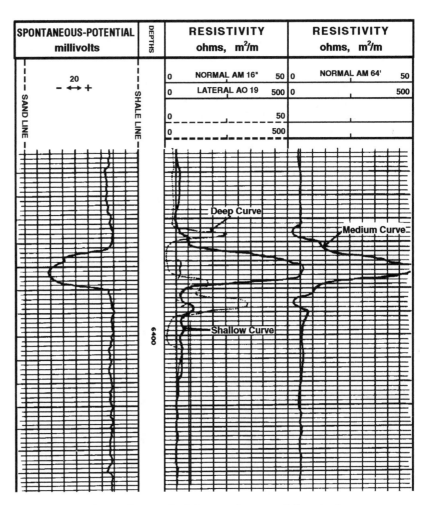

Figure 4.6. The SP log on the left records natural electrical currents flowing from sand and shale. When the curve is closer to the sandline, it indicates a sandy formation; when closer to the shale line, shale is present. The resistivity log on the right records the same formation's resistivity to an induced current.

Other electric logs are the caliper log and the dipmeter survey. A caliper is often run in with other logging tools to measure the diameter of the open hole, tubing, or casing (fig. 4.7).

It has spring-driven arms that press against the wall of the hole and move in and out with the changes in wellbore diameter. The tool senses and records an electrical signal that corresponds to the movement of the arms. It is useful for revealing caved-in or washed-out spots and corrosion, scale, or pits on the casing wall.

A *dipmeter survey* shows the direction and angle of dips in formations in relation to the wellbore (fig. 4.8). It is valuable because, if a well is not productive, a dipmeter survey may show that drilling a well in another location would produce more hydrocarbons. Hydrocarbons tend to accumulate high up (updip) in the formation, because they tend to move upward.

Radioactivity Logs

Like electric logs, *radioactivity logs* (also called nuclear logs) record either natural radioactivity or radioactive particles sent through the formation.

Gamma Ray Logs

A *gamma ray log* records gamma particles, often called gamma rays, that the formation gives off. The intensity of the gamma rays varies in different rocks, so this log reveals what types of rock are adjacent to the hole.

A *nuclear tracer* is a gas, liquid, or solid material that emits gamma rays. When a tracer is injected into any part of the well, its location or movement can be detected by a gamma ray detector. Sometimes

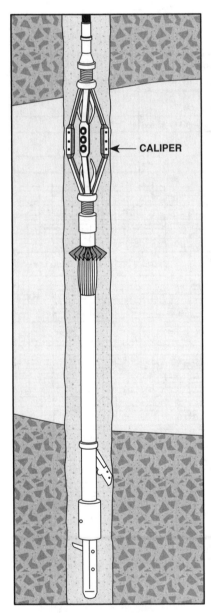

Figure 4.7. Calipers measure the diameter of the open hole, tubing, or casing.

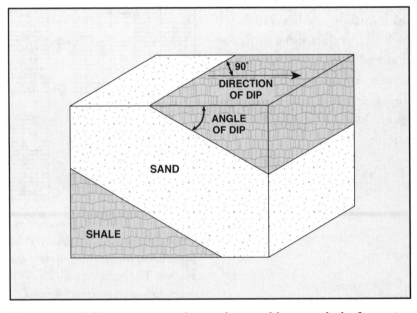

Figure 4.8. A dipmeter survey shows where and how much the formation dips in relation to the wellbore.

the tracer is mixed with cement to determine whether and/or where channels exist or to detect movement of cement behind casing before it hardens. Liquid tracers can reveal permeability as they travel through the formation. Yet another way of using a nuclear tracer is by using special charges containing a tracer in a perforating gun. The tracer leaves gamma radiation in the perforated holes. When the produced fluids pass through the holes, they carry the tracer away. Later, a gamma detector can show which holes the fluids flowed through.

Neutron Logs

To obtain a neutron log, a sonde sends atomic particles called neutrons through the formation. When they collide with hydrogen molecules, a detector records a decrease of neutrons. Few neutrons means a lot of hydrogen, which is the main component of water and hydrocarbons. A log shows how much oil and gas may be in the formation and its porosity. A special type of neutron survey, the pulsed neutron survey, also reveals how much water is in the reservoir fluid, movement of the water, and its salinity (how salty it is). The sonde and the log look similar to an acoustic or electric sonde and log.

Other types of neutron logging, such as density logging and salinity logging, bombard the rock with neutrons, which cause the formation to emit gamma rays. These may reveal porosity and the relative amounts of oil, gas, and salt water.

A *perforation depth control log*, or *PDC log*, is a combination radioactivity log and a *collar locator log* run into the well together (fig. 4.9). The collar locator measures and records the depth of each casing collar.

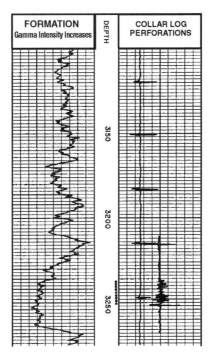

Figure 4.9. A perforation depth control (PDC) log shows the radioactivity curve on the left and the location of collars on the right. Together, they match formations containing hydrocarbons to depth.

Since the length of each joint of casing is written down, along with the number of joints of casing that were put into the well, knowing the number and depth of the collars allows an accurate measure of well depth. The radioactivity log locates hydrocarbons behind the casing. Using the information from both logs, the crew knows how deep the producing zone is and can determine exactly where to perforate casing.

Other Logs

A *temperature log* measures temperature in the hole. Drillers can locate the top of the cement in the annulus with a temperature log because cement generates heat as it sets. A temperature change can also indicate where a fluid in the well is seeping into the formation or leaking through a hole in the casing.

X-ray testing transmits X-rays or a radioactive tracer into the well. The X-rays or tracer emissions then expose a photographic film that can reveal corrosion and welding flaws in pipe.

A *spinner survey*, or *continuous flowmeter log*, measures flow rate and quantity in a producing well. The well fluids turn a small propeller. A recorder measures how fast the propeller turns and relates it to the amount and speed of the fluid. A spinner survey is particularly useful in gas wells.

A packer flowmeter uses an inflatable packer through which the well fluids flow. Since crew members know the exact depth of the packer, they can measure the flow rate at that depth.

PRODUCTION TESTING

Production tests help determine how much and how fast a well will produce. The company representative may run production tests before or after setting casing, cementing, and perforating.

Various tests measure formation pressures and the composition of formation fluids. A *bottomhole pressure test* uses a gauge to measure the pressure at or near the bottom of the well.

Pressure measurements can tell the company representative the most efficient rate of flow for the well.

Sampling formation fluids determines their composition. The percentages of oil, natural gas, and water in the fluids also help the company representative decide what the best completion method is for long-term, profitable production.

One of the most frequently performed production tests after completion is the potential test. A *potential test* measures the largest amount of gas and oil a well can produce over a 24-hour period under certain fixed conditions. Basically, the test involves allowing the well to produce for a given period of time and accurately measuring the production. Engineers use potential tests both when first producing the well and again several times during its life.

A *productivity test* combines a potential test and a bottom-hole pressure test to determine the effects of different flow rates on the pressure in the well.

This helps the company representative decide the rate at which the well should be produced for best results. Producing at the maximum flow rate may deplete the drive too quickly or damage the well.

A *wireline formation test* measures the pressures at specific depths. The tester is a tool that the crew runs into the well on a conductor line, after determining the proper depth with an SP log. The tester perforates the casing in one or two places. A valve opens a testing chamber to let in fluid and record its pressure. Finally, a sample chamber opens and draws in a few gallons (or litres) of formation fluid to bring to the surface. This test is good for quick readings of pressures, confirming porosity and permeability data from other logs, and predicting general productivity.

5

ANALYZING A WELL

Working on an existing well to restore or increase oil and gas production is an important part of today's petroleum industry. Oil companies decide whether to service or work over a well based on two main factors: supplies of oil and gas, and their prices in the marketplace.

When oil prices are high, oil companies invest in drilling new wells because they expect to recover the costs quickly. In 1979 through the early 1980s, for example, oil sold for about $35 a barrel, and an average of about 3,000 wells a month were being drilled in the United States. In 1986, the price had dropped to about $10 a barrel, and only about 800 wells were being drilled a month in the United States. Fewer new wells means the proportion of older wells increases, and older wells need service or workover.

REASONS FOR SERVICE OR WORKOVER

A well that needs service or workover is not producing at all or is producing hydrocarbons at a rate not up to full potential. Six general types of problems may call for a service or workover contractor: (1) excessive gas production, (2) excessive water production, (3) poor production rates, (4) production of sand, (5) equipment failure, or (6) depleted reservoirs.

Excessive Gas Production

In wells with a gas-cap drive, the natural gas expands as liquids flow out (fig. 5.1). Originally, perforations in the casing are well below the gas cap, but eventually the gas cap expands below the perforations. The well then starts producing a lot of gas with the liquids. Excessive gas production depletes the gas, driving the oil out of the reservoir.

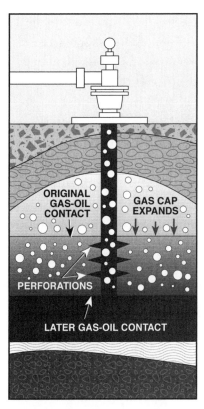

Figure 5.1. As oil is produced, the gas cap expands and reaches the level of the perforations in the casing or liner.

53

Excessive Water Production

In reservoirs with water drive, water is abundant, and it will often bypass the oil as it moves to the wellbore. As the hydrocarbons are pumped out, the water level rises and eventually reaches the perforations in the bottom of the wellbore (see fig. 1.7)—in the same way as the gas cap reaches down to the perforations. Both these conditions result in a well that produces a great deal of water and little oil. The ideal condition is to have the water-oil ratio equal zero, meaning that no water is produced with the oil. When more than one barrel of water is produced for every barrel of oil, however, the cost of producing the well rises. Too much water also creates a serious disposal problem because of Environmental Protection Agency regulations.

Generally speaking, excessive water production occurs because of fingering, fractures, or a poor cementing job around the production casing. Fingering occurs when the water moves through sections of the reservoir in "fingers" (fig 5.2) because of differing permeabilities in the reservoir. Fractures may also provide natural channels from a water-saturated reservoir to an oil-producing reservoir.

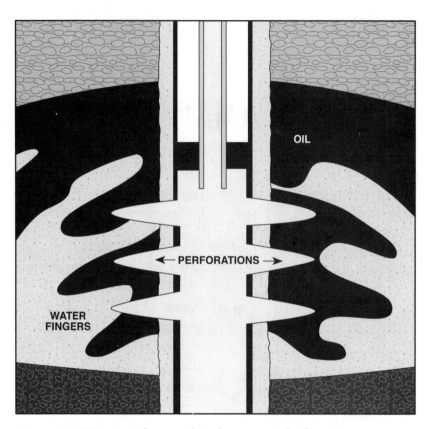

Figure 5.2. Water can bypass oil in the reservoir by fingering.

Poor Production Rate

Many problems can cause a well to produce below its full potential. Some are natural problems, such as reservoirs that have low permeability, low water-drive or gas-drive pressures, or oil that is too viscous (thick) to flow easily. For example, carbonate reservoir rocks are usually porous enough to store oil or gas, but they generally have a low permeability.

When the well is completed, it will not flow or will flow poorly because of its low permeability.

Artificial problems that were created during the drilling and completion phase of the well can cause a well to produce below its full potential. Sometimes drilling fluid makes the formation impermeable next to the wellbore. Or perforations may plug with casing debris, cement, and clay from the drilling mud and reduce the producing rate.

Production of Sand

Wells drilled through sandstone in which the sand grains are not fully cemented produce sand with hydrocarbons. Geologists classify the sand grains in sandstones as well-cemented, partially cemented, or not cemented (unconsolidated). Unconsolidated reservoirs, buried in basins adjacent to the Gulf of Mexico and the Pacific Coast, produce sand most often. Since these areas contain most of the United States' offshore producing fields, sand production is one of the major reasons for workovers in U.S. offshore wells.

Sand causes severe problems in a well because it can block almost any point in the flow stream. It can also destroy production equipment through abrasion. The amount of damage generally depends on the flow rate—the faster the reservoir fluid flows, the more sand it can carry and the more damage the sand will inflict, like sandblasting paint off a wall.

Equipment Failure

Mechanical failures of well equipment are common. Equipment failures can be divided into two groups: equipment malfunctions, and equipment leaks. Malfunctions most often occur in artificial-lift equipment such as beam pumps, submersible pumps, and gas-lift valves. Pumps and valves can simply wear out from prolonged use, and they need to be replaced periodically.

Downhole equipment leaks generally occur in the tubing, the casing, or the packer. Natural gas often contains carbon dioxide and compounds of sulfur, such as hydrogen sulfide. These compounds combine with water to form acids that are highly corrosive to metal and rubber. Constant exposure to corrosive fluids can eat holes in the tubing, casing, or packer seal. Tubing can also develop a leak as the sucker rod string moves up and down inside it. Rod couplings, which are the widest part of the string, may rub against the side of the tubing.

Leaks in downhole equipment cause two problems. Most important, a leak in the tubing is a safety hazard. A hole in the tubing allows oil or gas to get into the annular space between the tubing and casing, which applies pressure to the casing at the surface. The danger occurs if the fluid or gas pressure exceeds the pressure rating of the wellhead equipment. The second problem is loss of production due to oil or gas escaping through the hole.

Depleted Reservoirs

In the Gulf Coast and Pacific Coast regions of the United States, one well may produce hydrocarbons from several reservoirs, one on top of the next (fig. 5.3). It is customary in this case to produce one reservoir at a time, beginning with the deepest one. Eventually, all the oil or gas in that reservoir is depleted. A workover crew then seals off the lower, depleted reservoir and opens up the next shallower reservoir.

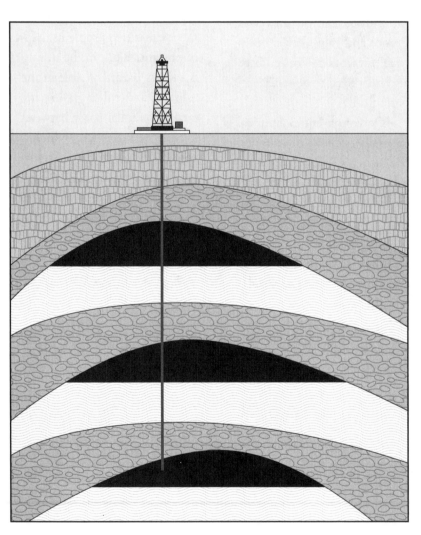

Figure 5.3. Several reservoirs may be stacked. A well may produce from the deepest reservoir first, then be sealed off and produce from a higher reservoir.

ANALYZING A POORLY PRODUCING WELL

When a well's production slows or stops, the oil company, or lease operator, analyzes the well to decide the best course of action. Analyzing the well to decide what is wrong before starting any operation lowers the risk of investing money in a well that is not likely to produce much more and determines the best course for workover.

The oil company or operator considers three possible courses of action: (1) work on the well, (2) abandon the well, or (3) do nothing. An investigation includes a study of the well's mechanical history, geologic data and reservoir conditions, past performance, and well servicing and workover histories. Agencies that regulate the petroleum industry now largely govern whether and how long a lease operator can do nothing.

Mechanical History

Studying the well's mechanical status at the time it stopped producing sometimes quickly identifies the problem. This step determines whether any downhole equipment has failed to function or has worn out. The lease operator checks the casing, the tubing, the packers, the perforations, any gas-lift valves, the liner, and the gravel pack. Equipment failures are generally the easiest of all well problems to pinpoint because some operation will cease.

Geologic Data and Reservoir Conditions

Studying the underground geology of the oilfield will help determine whether the reservoir is capable of further flow. In most developed producing areas, geologists have compiled a large body of data based on the analysis of cores, reservoir fluids, and logs. They also usually have contour maps, cross sections, and sand-thickness maps.

They compare the amount of hydrocarbons that has already been recovered with their original estimates of how much oil and gas the well would produce. If they believe enough hydrocarbons remain, they will recommend repairing the well. If, however, workover will not bring the well back up to an acceptable level of production, they use the information to predict the next producing zone in the field and plug the old one.

Past Performance

The amount of oil and gas the well has produced and how much reservoir energy it took to produce them are valuable information. The reservoir's pressure history charts the rise and fall of well pressures. Ideally, the curve slopes downward steadily, showing a steady decrease in pressure. In reality, there may be sudden losses or increases in pressure, as various upsets occur. For example, the wellhead may have failed, causing a sudden loss in pressure.

Or, production may have been shut in to make a repair, causing a sudden increase in pressure. The pressure curve shows whether the reservoir has enough energy to continue to produce.

The production and pressure histories of a well that has stopped producing help analysts determine whether the well is not producing because the hydrocarbons are gone or because the reservoir drive is depleted.

Well Servicing and Workover History

A review of the well servicing and workover history of a well reveals whether it has had similar producing problems in the past. If it has had the same sort of problem before, looking at its history can reveal any difficulties that previous repair crews encountered. For example, perhaps removing the downhole equipment was very difficult.

The tubing was very corroded, and every time the crew pulled it, a portion broke off. This type of information helps analysts to estimate how long it will take to repair the well and evaluate the risk involved in doing the work. Analysis of past jobs can prevent the same mistakes from happening again and can identify which repairs or workover methods previous crews tried that failed to make any difference in performance.

Once the production specialists have identified the well's problem, they decide on a course of action. First, they design a plan to correct the problem and they then formulate a work plan for the service or workover crew to use.

6

=SERVICE AND WORKOVER EQUIPMENT=

Before the 1950s, rig builders usually built a permanent derrick at each well for drilling and maintenance of the well throughout its life. Now, however, the whole drilling rig is moved to a new site when drilling is finished. The well is left with only a wellhead and sometimes a pump, so service and workover companies must bring the equipment they need to work in the well.

The amount and type of equipment they need depends on the job. One job may require a light-duty rig and a couple of workers. The next well may need a somewhat larger rig with a tall mast and a crew of several workers. Another job may require extra crews to work around the clock and a rig capable of light drilling and heavy-duty hoisting.

RIG EQUIPMENT

Service and workover rigs, like drilling rigs, are machines for hoisting pipe, wireline, and tools into and out of a well. They have a derrick or mast, a drawworks, and a power source. Unlike drilling rigs, not all of them have circulation or rotary systems.

They come in a variety of sizes. In general, servicing jobs require smaller rigs than workover jobs. The smallest rigs raise and lower a wireline or conductor line. Oilfield workers sometimes call these wireline rigs (fig. 6.1).

Figure 6.1. A small, light-duty unit

59

Medium-duty rigs can pull
sucker rods or a lightweight
string of tubing (fig. 6.2). The
heaviest rigs are workover rigs
for drilling and deep well work
(fig. 6.3).

The rig size determines how
much weight it can hoist. A
wireline with a tool attached to
the end of it weighs much less
than tubing, and tubing weighs
less than drill pipe. Weight of
the *work string* (the pipe string
that holds whatever tool the
crew is using) also determines
how deep a well the rig can
service—a deeper well requires
a longer work string, which is
heavier. For example, a rig large
enough for a 15,000-foot (4,500-
metre) servicing job using tubing is only large enough for,
maybe, a 10,000-foot (3,000-
metre) workover job using
heavier drill pipe.

Figure 6.2. A medium-duty unit

Figure 6.3. A large, heavy-duty unit

Masts

Although no service or workover rig has a derrick (because it is portable, it always has a mast), both manufacturers and oilfield personnel often call a mast a derrick.

The mast rests horizontally on top of the unit that transports it (in the headache position) until time to set up the rig over the well (fig. 6.4). Then the crew raises the mast to the vertical position, usually with a hydraulic ram (fig. 6.5), or, rarely, using a wire rope. At this point, the mast is only half its full height. Its two sections are either folded or, more commonly, telescoped one inside the other. The crew extends the top section with the hydraulic ram. A mechanical device at the top of the lower part of the mast locks the two sections firmly together to make a solid

Figure 6.4. The mast is in the horizontal, or headache, position while being transported.

Figure 6.5. A hydraulic ram raises the mast to the vertical position.

structure. The full height of the mast may be from 35 to over 100 feet (10.6 to over 30 metres). The most common size for working with tubing is a double derrick, or doubles rig, one high enough to work with a stand of two joints at a time (fig. 6.6). A stand consists of the connected joints of pipe ready to be raised out of or lowered into the well. A stand may be a single, double, thribble, or fourble, depending on the number of joints.

To stabilize the mast, one guy line often goes from the top of the mast to the front of the carrier and other lines connect it to anchors around the rig (fig. 6.7). Each anchor works like a drywall anchor you use in your home to attach a bolt to sheetrock. It has arms that fold up against the shank as it is pushed into a 6- to 8-foot (1.8- to 2.4-metre) hole in the ground. When it reaches the bottom, the arms fold out,

Figure 6.6. A doubles rig is tall and strong enough for stands of two joints screwed together, or doubles.

Figure 6.7. Guy lines from mast to carrier and from mast to anchors in the ground stabilize the mast.

so that to pull the anchor out would mean pulling up all the earth on top of the arms.

Members (or girts) that make up the mast may be tubular (fig. 6.8A) or angular (fig. 6.8B) steel pieces. Depending on engineering design, both the tubular and the angular steel mast may be of comparable strength.

Prime Mover

The power source, or prime mover, for the hoisting system is either the engine of the truck that carries the rig or a separate diesel engine that directly powers the drawworks or runs a generator to drive an electric motor. Heavy-duty workover rigs may have two engines to provide more power.

Drawworks

The drawworks on a service or workover rig, like the one on a drilling rig, is a variation on the simple windlass or winch. The horsepower of the prime mover, the strength of the mast, and the braking capacity determine how much weight the drawworks can hoist.

Figure 6.8. A pole mast (A) is constructed of tubular members. A structural mast (B) is constructed of angular members.

RIG TRANSPORT

Manufacturers build service and workover rigs on three different types of bases for transporting on land. Which base they use depends in part on the weight and size of the equipment it must carry. Deeper wells require masts that are stronger and heavier, larger drawworks drums, and more engine power; therefore, the rig needs a stronger base.

The smallest rigs usually rest on specially built trucks, larger rigs sit on trailers pulled by tractors, and many are basically rigs on wheels with a steering mechanism, called carrier rigs. Portable rigs are relatively easy to move and quick to assemble in the oilfield.

Truck-Mounted Rigs

A truck-mounted rig (also called a truck-mounted unit or truck-mounted hoist) looks somewhat like a flatbed truck loaded with equipment (fig. 6.9). Truck-mounted hoists are used for servicing shallow to medium-depth wells—up to about 9,000 feet (about 2,740 metres) deep. The masts on truck-mounted rigs are only tall enough to handle a single joint of tubing or two sucker rods, so they are limited to light-duty service. They have no rotary or circulation equipment. The truck's engine powers the drawworks.

The mast on a truck-mounted rig often does not require guy wires to hold it vertical, but has hydraulic jacks, or braces, to stabilize it.

Figure 6.9. A truck-mounted rig

Trailer Rigs

A trailer rig is a tractor-trailer vehicle (fig. 6.10). It is a heavier rig that may have a longer mast, a rotary, and one or two engines. Whereas the truck engine powers the hoisting system on a truck-mounted unit, on a trailer rig the prime mover powers the rig systems and propels the vehicle when it is on the road.

CARRIER RIGS

A carrier rig (also called carrier unit or self-propelled unit) looks like a platform full of machinery on wheels (figs. 6.11 and 6.12). It is difficult to tell at a glance which end is the front.

Like a trailer rig, the prime mover powers a carrier rig on the road. Steering gear and a cab for the driver convert the

rig to a self-propelled vehicle. The advantages of carrier rigs are better weight distribution on the wheels and more powerful engine-transmission combinations. Even though the largest workover rigs are nearly always carrier rigs, even light- to medium-duty service and workover rigs may be built this way.

Manufacturers offer two styles of carrier rigs. In one, the bottom of the mast is attached to the rear of the unit, opposite the driver's cab. Manufacturers call this a *back-in unit* (see fig. 6.11) because the driver must back it into place. Drive-in units have the driver's cab and the mast base on the same end (see fig. 6.12). The driver can see the well better when positioning a drive-in unit. Its disadvantage, however, is that the oil and dirt that inevitably accumulate around the wellhead will cover the cab's windows.

Carrier rigs may have one or two engines. Built-in hydraulic pumps raise the mast and power the auxiliary equipment. Some units have hydraulic leveling jacks to speed rig-up on uneven ground.

Figure 6.10. A tractor pulls a trailer rig carrying prime movers.

Figure 6.11. A back-in carrier rig's cab is opposite the bottom of the mast.

Figure 6.12. A drive-in carrier unit's cab is on the same end as the bottom of the mast.

SPECIALTY RIGS

Service and workover rigs come in many variations to allow work on wells in any possible environment and use different combinations or types of equipment.

All-Terrain Units

Because the search for oil has led to remote areas with severe weather or difficult terrain and no highways, such as the Arctic, swamps, deserts, jungles, and mountains, manufacturers have begun producing carrier rigs with equipment designed for specific difficult conditions.

Options include a steering system that allows tight turns, a heavy-duty cooling system and air cleaners to filter sand, oversized tires or tracks like a military tank for off-road transport, or an enclosure around the working area to protect the crew from extreme cold. Some workover rigs can even be disassembled into sections for transport by helicopter (fig. 6.13).

Slant-Hole Rigs

For wells that have been drilled on a slant rather than straight down, service and workover companies use a special rig called a slant-hole rig (fig. 6.14). It has a mast that can move forward and back as well as side to side so that the crew can adjust it to the angle of the wellbore.

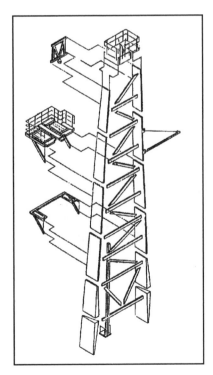

Figure 6.13. Rigs designed to be moved by helicopter can be broken down into component packages.

Figure 6.14. The mast on this slant-hole rig is tilted to 45°, its maximum tilt.

Spudders

A *spudder* is a portable drilling rig mounted on a truck or trailer. Instead of drilling by rotating a bit, it drills by repeatedly dropping a sharp, pointed bit onto the rock. It is no longer common as a drilling rig, but service and workover companies may still use a spudder to work on shallow wells. Spudders never have pumping equipment, so contractors do not use them in wells that require a fluid to control well pressure. The advantage of a spudder is that a crew can move it in, rig it up, and be ready to work in a few hours.

Offshore Rigs

On a platform well with a permanent rig, no special service or workover rig is necessary—the crew uses the drilling rig. On offshore wells drilled by mobile rigs that have since moved on, ships or barges carry service and workover rigs to the well (fig. 6.15). Some workover barge rigs have carefully designed hulls to support light-duty drilling machinery.

Because space is always limited at offshore wells, the masts do not need guy lines and may be raised by power from the drawworks instead of a hydraulic ram.

COILED TUBING UNITS

Coiled tubing is exactly what it sounds like: flexible tubing that can be coiled onto a drum and uncoiled for placement into a well for many servicing and workover jobs. Coiled tubing usually has a small diameter, ¾ to 2⅜ inches (19 to 60 millimetres). Service and workover crews use it in the same way they use wireline and regular tubing—to lower tools into the well and circulate fluids. Coiled tubing is run into the well in one piece inside the normal tubing.

Figure 6.15.   Offshore service and workover rig

A coiled tubing unit is usually mounted on a trailer or skid, a platform that can be set on a trailer or barge (fig. 6.16). Components of the unit include a reel for coiled tubing, an injector head to push tubing down the well, a wellhead blowout preventer stack, a power source (usually a diesel engine and hydraulic pumps), and a control console. The reel can carry up to 20,000 feet (6,100 metres) of coiled tubing, enough to reach the bottom of most wells.

Using a coiled tubing unit instead of a workover rig is faster and less expensive than running conventional, jointed tubing on many jobs. It also allows the crew to work on the well without killing it, or stopping production by circulating a very heavy drilling mud into the well. Coiled tubing is valuable in horizontal wells, where it is impossible to use a wireline (which would be like pushing a cooked noodle). Although coiled tubing technology has been around since the 1960s, the bugs are only now being worked out of it so that it is becoming more popular.

AUXILIARY TOOLS AND EQUIPMENT

Like workover and service rigs, auxiliary tools and equipment are mobile. Some workover operations are around-the-clock jobs. In this case, house trailers and provisions for the crews are standard auxiliary equipment.

Auxiliary equipment for well servicing and workover rigs includes tongs to screw and unscrew lengths of pipe, racks to store pipe, a top drive or rotary to rotate tubing (see figs. 1.15 and 1.17), pumping equipment, and blowout preventers.

Tongs

Tongs are large wrenches the crew uses to make up (screw) or break out (unscrew) lengths of tubing, casing, or other pipe. Manual tongs are operated using the catshaft—a special shaft rotated by the drawworks. Power tongs are pneumatically or hydraulically operated; that is, they operate using compressed air or hydraulic pressure.

Figure 6.16. This coiled tubing unit is mounted on a trailer.

A catshaft is a shaft on the drawworks with catheads on each end (fig. 6.17). Catheads are small devices that reel in a wire rope or a chain. To use manual tongs, a crew member sets the tongs to grip the joint. The driller then activates a cathead to reel in the wire rope or chain attached to the tongs (fig. 6.18). Rotating the shaft and catheads spools up the rope or chain, which then pulls on the tongs to tighten or loosen the joint.

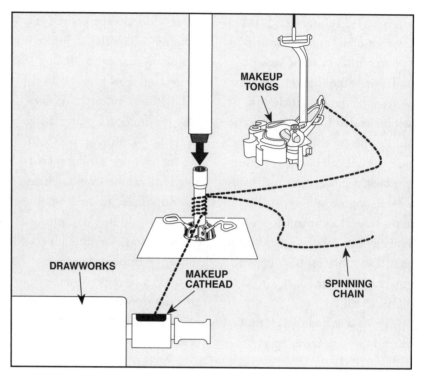

Figure 6.17. Rope or chain wrapped around the catheads is attached to manual tongs. Spooling the rope up pulls on the tongs.

Figure 6.18. A chain or a line from the cathead attaches to a long handle on manual tongs to make up and break out pipe.

Power tongs incorporate a small hydraulic motor and transmission (fig. 6.19). The motor often works at variable speeds that can spin a threaded joint of pipe rapidly at first and then slowly tighten it into the coupling at a measured torque, or turning force. Some types automatically disengage when the threads are not aligned properly.

Figure 6.19. Power tongs use a hydraulic motor.

Figure 6.20.   The crew stores tubing joints on racks near the mast.

Pipe and Rod Storage

When a service or workover
crew pulls tubing or casing out
of a well, crew members must
have a place to store the joints
as they break them out. Drilling rigs often have racks that
are stationary (fig. 6.20). Trans-
portable storage units for pipe
are mounted on trailers or self-
propelled mobile units (similar
to carrier rigs). Hydraulic cranes
move the pipe from the rack to
the floor of the rig.

To move sucker rods, a sub elevator picks them up and transfers them to or from the rod hanger (fig. 6.21). A rod hanger is exactly what it sounds like: a device that hangs the rods on the mast or derrick.

Pumping Equipment

Some workover jobs require circulation of a fluid, the workover fluid, similar to drilling mud. Rigs for these jobs include a mud pump with its own engine and a tank for mixing dry ingredients with water or oil to make the mud.

Blowout Preventers

A *blowout* is an uncontrolled flow of gas, oil, or water—or all three—from a well. A blowout frequently sends debris flying through the air or catches the well on fire or both. Needless to say, this is very dangerous to anyone working on the well. Blowouts can occur before casing is set or long after drilling, when the well is being serviced or repaired.

Figure 6.21. Sucker rods hang on a rod hanger in the mast.

Blowout preventers (BOPs) shut off a well while it is being drilled or serviced and allow the well to be closed in with or without pipe in the hole. A well with a beam pumping unit always has a blowout preventer that closes the space around the polished rod. Whenever crew members pull tubing, they install blowout preventers on the wellhead.

One type of preventer for servicing and workover is a ram blowout preventer (fig. 6.22). A ram preventer closes in the space around a string of pipe or wireline or the polished rod of a sucker rod assembly in the well. It does this by moving rams—pieces of metal that move back and forth with a strong force.

Rams operate in pairs and each set fits only one size of wireline, drill pipe, tubing, polished rod, or coiled tubing. Each ram is faced with a sealing element that closes in the well when the ram faces contact each other. Although rams of different sizes can be exchanged in a blowout preventer, a crew may stack more than one ram preventer over the well to accommodate more than one size of pipe or wireline. Most ram preventers today operate hydraulically, using a fluid under pressure in a cylinder to close the rams, but some are manually operated. They also have screws to lock the rams in the closed position.

An *annular preventer* (fig. 6.23) uses a ring of reinforced synthetic rubber instead of rams to seal the opening. Annular preventers can be shut in to seal off any size pipe. They also may be hydraulically or manually operated, but cannot be locked mechanically, as ram preventers can.

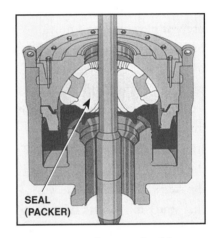

Figure 6.23. An annular blowout preventer uses a rubber seal to fit any size pipe.

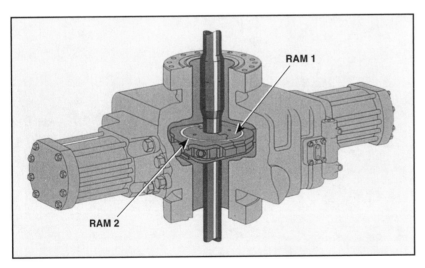

Figure 6.22. A ram blowout preventer has rams that fit snugly against pipe or wireline going into the well.

SERVICING AND WORKOVER FLUIDS

Some workover procedures besides drilling use a circulating fluid in the well. In drilling, the fluid removes cuttings, cools the bit, and supports the walls of the hole until casing is set. In workover jobs, the fluid may circulate sand out of the well, prevent blowouts, and provide hydraulic power for downhole tools, as well as serve as a drilling fluid. In both drilling and workover, one of the fluid's main functions is to offset the pressure of the formation. Fluid in the hole exerts pressure against the sidewalls, in the same way that water in a plastic swimming pool pushes the sides of the pool outward.

Circulating fluid used during servicing and workovers is usually either salt water or a specially mixed drilling mud called workover fluid. Workover crews very often use the saltwater in the formation as the workover fluid because it is available and does not damage the formation. Some other fluids can cause particles of shale in the producing formation to swell. Swollen particles plug up the tiny channels that make the rock permeable, so oil and gas cannot escape into the well as easily.

Workover fluid, like drilling mud, can be water-based or oil-based. Additives may include barium sulfate (barite) and clay. Barite is a heavy mineral powder that increases the weight of the fluid. A heavier fluid presses more against the formation than a lighter fluid or water will. Adding a pulverized clay raises the viscosity of the fluid, that is, makes it flow more slowly. Particles of clay also coat, or plaster, the walls of the hole, much as stucco plasters the walls of a room. This coating stabilizes an open hole and prevents permeable formations from absorbing liquid in the workover fluid.

7

WELL SERVICING AND REPAIR

Wells require maintenance and repairs from time to time due to normal wear, age, and hazards of the environment to which the equipment is exposed. Downhole pumps, sucker rods, and gas-lift equipment all have moving parts, which wear out because of erosion from the fast-moving reservoir fluid, which may contain sand or particles of metal left from perforating, for example. Production tubing also corrodes. Both moving and stationary equipment can fail because of corrosion, scale, and paraffin deposits.

Lease operators are usually the first to notice abnormal conditions in the well that suggest the need for repair work. Routine tests and well reports on daily production, wellhead pressure, and percentage of water in the oil provide evidence of the need for maintenance or repair.

The most common service and repair jobs include swabbing and repairing or replacing sucker rod pumps, sucker rods, production tubing, and packers. (The next chapter describes another type of servicing job, fishing.)

REPAIRING BEAM PUMPING EQUIPMENT

Modern beam pumping units perform for a long time with proper care and when not overloaded. Proper care means regular lubrication of the moving parts and seasonal changes of the oil in the speed reducer. Many rig operators choose not to change the oil unless it appears to be dirty; however, they pull the drain plug on the speed reducer to drain any condensation.

Another maintenance check is to assure that the cranks are correctly counterbalanced. Improper weight can cause damage to the gear teeth.

Sucker Rods and Pumps

Sucker rods, their couplings, and sucker rod pumps can fail because of corrosion and scale, erosion and wear, careless handling, or stress from the pump's movement. Often, more than one of these factors is at work.

To service, repair, or replace the rods or pump, a crew pulls the sucker rod string out of the well. For a tubing pump crew members must also pull the tubing, and for an insert pump they pull only the sucker rod string.

Corrosion, Scale, and Paraffin Deposits

Sucker rods and pumps (and also the tubing and casing) corrode because of several different kinds of reactions (fig. 7.1). The most familiar is rust, caused when oxygen from the air gets into the well fluids.

Hydrogen sulfide causes sour corrosion, a very severe type. The metal becomes brittle and cracks. Certain bacteria that live in the absence of free oxygen produce products that form corrosive hydrogen sulfide.

Carbon dioxide from the formation causes sweet corrosion, sharp and deep pitting, sometimes with a worm-eaten or grooved appearance. Carbon dioxide reacts with moisture in a well to form carbonic acid, which in turn reacts with the iron in steel to form a hard black scale that adheres to the metal. This scale creates galvanic corrosion from the iron to the scale.

Galvanic corrosion, or electrolysis, occurs when an electrical current flows from one piece of metal to another. The two pieces of metal and the surrounding fluid actually create a battery.

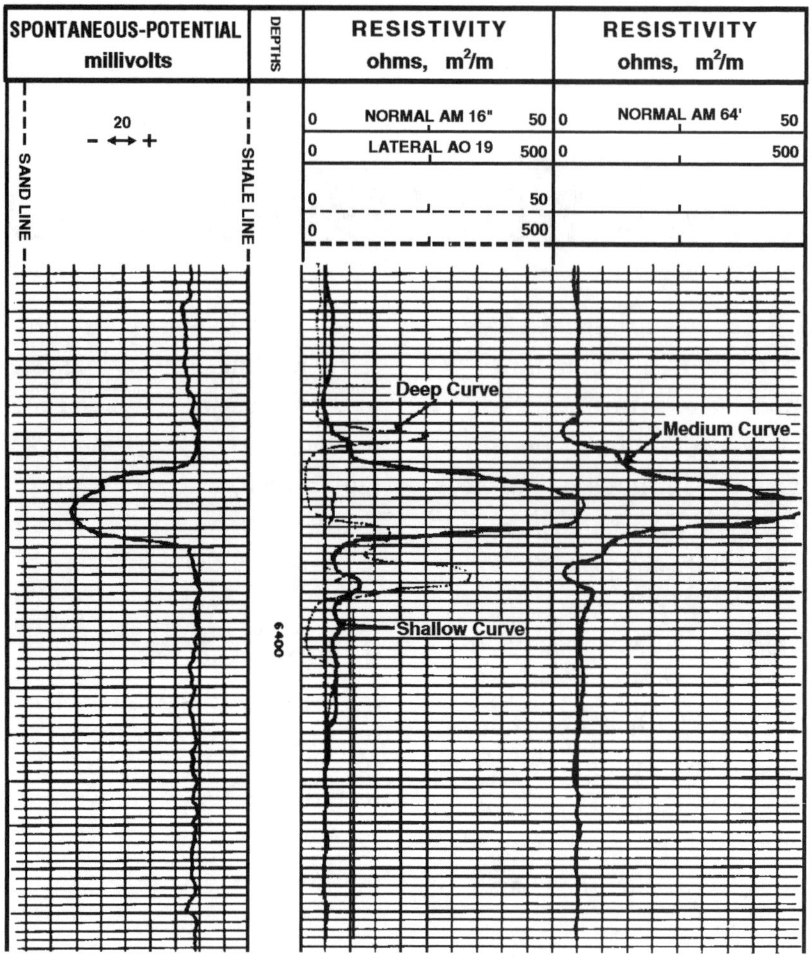

Figure 7.1. Conventional electric log showing an SP curve and short normal, medium normal, and standard lateral curves.

Besides scale, other sources of galvanic corrosion may be two pieces of equipment made of different metals, such as dissimilar joints of tubing. This type of corrosion can severely damage a sucker rod string very quickly.

Paraffin forms deposits in a well that are the same as the paraffin wax in candles. Paraffin is a hydrocarbon; its lighter forms are methane and ethane, which flow out with the oil. Its heavier forms, however, can clog up the perforations in the gas anchor of the rod pump.

Service crews can often remove scale and paraffin deposits by circulating a chemical that dissolves them. When a rod or the pump corrodes, however, they must be replaced.

Erosion and Wear

A metal surface erodes or abrades when a turbulent flow of fluids wears it away, like a fast-flowing river rounds a rock (fig. 7.2). When the fluid is clean, bubbles form that pound against the metal. A fluid contaminated with solids such as salts and sand erodes a metal surface even faster. Erosion can combine with corrosion to attack metal. As erosion abrades the metal, it exposes new metal to corrode away. Eventually the rod, coupling, or pump part breaks.

Wear results from friction, when two metal surfaces rub together. When the completion or workover crew makes up the sucker rod string, crew members lubricate each thread, but extreme pressure can squeeze the lubricant out. Friction then wears out the unlubricated thread and it breaks.

Careless Handling

The crew should do everything possible to handle the sucker rods so as to prevent stress risers. A *stress riser* is any bend, nick, dent, hammer mark, or pit in the rod. Each of these concentrates any destructive force that is present on that spot. The stress riser causes that part of the rod to break sooner than an undamaged part would.

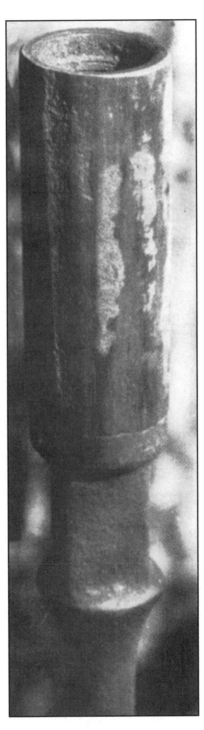

Figure 7.2. Abrasion has damaged this coupling.

Many sucker rods have a relatively soft coating of a special steel alloy that protects them from corrosion. Any break in this coating, caused by a hammer mark for instance, exposes the metal underneath and leaves a spot for corrosion to attack. The corrosion then produces pits that weaken the rod.

Range of Load

Range of load is the difference in load, or force, on the rod string between the upstroke and the downstroke. Because of the way the pump's valves work, the sucker rod string relaxes slightly with each downstroke and snaps tight at the beginning of every upstroke. The faster the stroke and the heavier the fluid, the more violent is the snapping. This shock can break rods.

Coupling and Pin Failures

Manufacturing improvements, better design, and higher-grade materials have increased the amount of stress that rods can handle. These improvements in rod technology can also lead to worse problems with coupling failures because of heavy loading, however. The couplings are the weakest points in a rod string. The weight of the string itself, the pump, and the fluid being pumped are more likely to break the couplings than the rods.

One common problem is that a coupling and pin (the threaded end of the rod) can disconnect. Sometimes the pin or coupling breaks because it has been overtightened or undertightened. Overtightening stretches the neck of the pin and weakens it (fig. 7.3A). Overtightening also can cause the end of the coupling to flare out and ruin the coupling (fig. 7.3B).

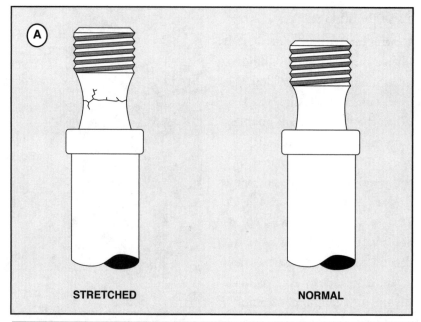

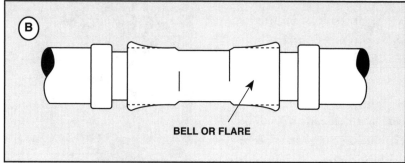

Figure 7.3. (A) Overtightening stretches the neck of the pin, which causes it to weaken and break. (B) Overtightening can also cause the end of the coupling to flare out.

Undertightening or loosening of the pin and coupling while in use cracks and eventually breaks either the pin or the coupling. Corrosion can accelerate this type of failure. The coupling, although it is the heaviest section of the sucker rod string, may also fail because of range of load.

Because pins and couplings account for most rod breaks, one manufacturer produces a flexible, continuous sucker rod. It has only two couplings, one at the polished rod and one at the pump. It is transported to the well on reels that are 18 feet (5.5 metres) in diameter. Continuous sucker rod is useful particularly in crooked and directional wells.

REPAIRING PRODUCTION TUBING AND PACKERS

A service crew can usually replace a packer fairly easily, but pulling tubing is a bigger job that requires a heavier rig. The same types of corrosion that damage sucker rods—sweet and sour corrosion, rust, and galvanic corrosion—also damage tubing. Sometimes the corrosion is so bad that the tubing partially or completely collapses.

Paraffin deposits along the walls can reduce the inside diameter of the tubing so that production slows, the rod string hangs up in the tubing, or the tools cannot be run in. The crew can clean out the tubing by running a paraffin cutter in on a wireline. The paraffin cutter will remove a small amount of paraffin from the tubing with each run until it has cleaned the tubing of paraffin. Another method is to pump a chemical down the hole that will dissolve paraffin or scale.

Over time, various deposits, such as from corrosion, salt, and gypsum, can build up and reduce the internal diameter of the casing. These deposits may be cleaned and pushed to bottom with a casing scraper, which has blades around its circumference that are spring-loaded to press against the casing wall (fig. 7.4).

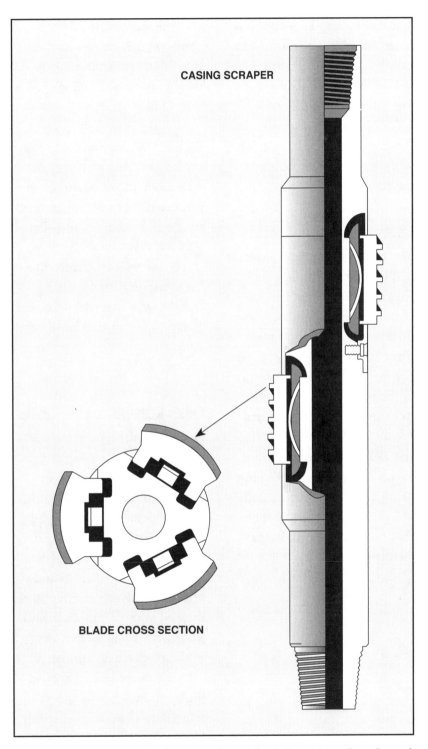

CASING SCRAPER

BLADE CROSS SECTION

Figure 7.4. A scraper's blades clean the inside of the casing when the tool either rotates or moves up or down.

The scraper may be rotated if it is run on tubing, or moved vertically if it is run on a wireline. Where there is a buildup of any foreign matter on the casing wall, this procedure usually clears the path for successful running of a packer or other tools into the casing.

Leaks

The tubing string must be intact and seal tightly over its entire length to contain the pressure of the formation fluids flowing up through it and to prevent them from leaking into the space between the tubing and the casing. It must be strong enough to withstand not only internal pressure without breaking, but also external pressure from the packer fluid without collapsing. Leaks may develop in the middle of a tubing joint, but most often they occur in the couplings at each end.

A manufacturing defect or corrosion may cause a leak, or the rod string can wear a hole if it rubs against the tubing's inside wall. While not serious at first, small leaks in the tubing string get bigger because of the pressure on the leak. A 3,000-foot (900-metre) column of oil, for example, exerts over 1,000 pounds per square inch (about 7,000 kPa) of pressure at bottom.

Some company representatives routinely test for tubing leaks in wells that use sucker rod pumps. They usually hire a company that specializes in pressure testing.

Other Reasons to Pull Tubing

Sometimes the repair crew has to pull the tubing string even though the tubing itself is in good condition, for example, if a packer fails. It may also be necessary to pull the tubing if it fills with sand for a considerable distance above the bottom of the hole. In this case, pressure trapped in the string is a hazard, since serious injuries may occur as the joints are unscrewed. If crew members notice gas escaping when they first loosen a joint, they allow the pressure to bleed off before unscrewing the joint all the way.

Repairing Packers

Packers fail for the same reasons the pump and sucker rods do: corrosion and erosion. The repair crew pulls retrievable packers simply by pulling the tubing out of the hole. Repair usually involves replacing the resilient sealing element and other worn parts. To replace a nonretrievable packer, the crew drills it out with a milling tool and sets a new one.

WELLHEAD REPAIRS

Sometimes service crews repair or replace wellhead fittings or pipe connections before doing other work. In the case of a naturally flowing well, they may need to repair only a damaged valve or other fitting. If the well uses a beam pump, however, repairs may be complicated. They may have to replace the rod blowout preventer, polished rod stuffing box, or the polished rod itself.

The crew usually gets to this equipment by pulling the polished rod and removing the bridle from the horsehead of the pumping unit. The possibility of pressure in the space between the tubing and the casing presents a constant danger. Crew members always proceed with wellhead work cautiously, checking pressure at each stage and allowing it to bleed off.

UNLOADING THE WELL

To unload a well is to reduce the pressure in the production tubing or casing so that the formation pressure starts the hydrocarbons flowing. Unloading usually involves removing some of the liquid from the tubing. One way to do this is to run in coiled tubing to siphon off the liquid. The most common method, however, is swabbing.

As mentioned in Chapter 2, a newly completed well is often swabbed to start the flow. When a service or workover crew pulls the tubing, they kill the well (stop production) by pumping brine into it. To restart the flow, they swab it. Or the company representative may call in a swabbing rig (a light-duty service rig) for a producing well when formation pressure drops and production slows. Sometimes swabbing will restart the flow.

Swabbing crews use a wireline called a sandline or swabbing line from a small reel on the rig's drawworks to lower a swab assembly. The swab assembly fits inside the tubing or, less often, the casing. Raising the swab assembly pulls the brine up to the surface, like pulling a liquid into a syringe (fig. 7.5), and so lowers the pressure holding back the production flow. The brine then flows through a flow line connected to the side of the wellhead into a pit or tank for proper disposal.

The basic equipment for swabbing is a truck-mounted hoist with a short, telescoping mast. Additional equipment includes a swab assembly, a lubricator with an oil saver, and a shut-off valve on the well, also called a swabbing valve.

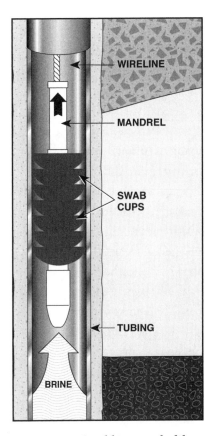

Figure 7.5. Swabbing works like a syringe to lower pressure in the wellbore.

Swab Assembly

A swab assembly (also called a swab) consists of a mandrel with swab cups on it and a weight, or sinker bar (fig. 7.6).

A swab cup is a cylinder made of or lined with natural or synthetic rubber (fig. 7.7). It wraps around a hollow metal mandrel, or shaft. The rubber is sometimes reinforced with wire or lined with an aluminum or steel sleeve for heavy loads. A swab has two, sometimes three, cups for a good seal. The cups may be smooth or ribbed on the outside (see fig. 7.6).

The mandrel may be steel or aluminum. It includes a valve that closes when the swab is raised to prevent fluid from leaking back down the tubing.

Because a swab can get stuck in the hole, the swabbing crew may use a special aluminum mandrel that connects to a steel sub (threaded connector; *sub* is short for "substitute") by means of a pin. If the swab gets stuck, crew members can break the pin. They can then dissolve the aluminum swab assembly with acid.

Most swab assemblies include a 5- to 20-foot (1.5- to 6-metre) sinker bar that weights the assembly so that it will run into the hole properly.

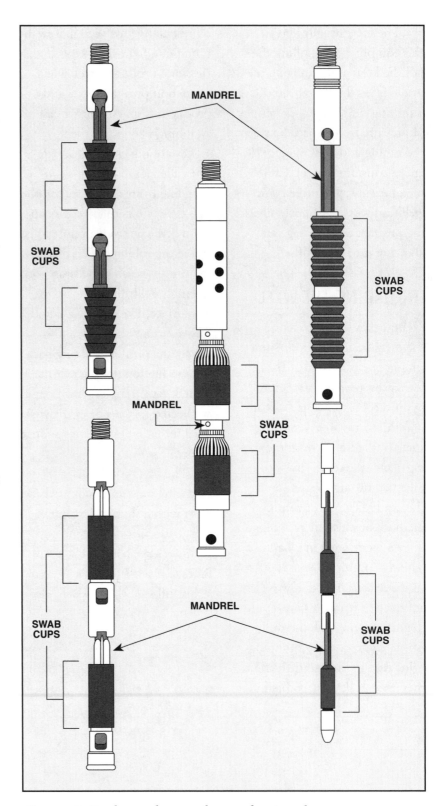

Figure 7.6. Swabs may have swab cups of various shapes.

Figure 7.7. Swab cups are made of or lined with natural or synthetic rubber.

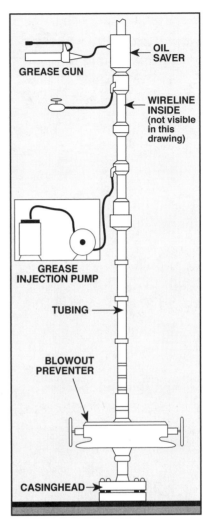

Figure 7.8. In a lubricator, an oil saver seals off pressure between the wireline and the tubing while allowing the wireline to move in and out.

Lubricator

A lubricator uses grease to form a seal between the wireline and the tubing or casing (fig. 7.8). It is made up of several joints of specially fabricated tubing (usually a blowout preventer) that fit above a valve on top of the casinghead or tubing head. It seals off pressure but still allows the wireline to move in and out.   A grease injection pump forces grease into the lubrica-tor to form a pressure-tight seal between the wireline and the inner wall of the lubricator's tubing. At the top of the lubricator is an oil saver. The oil saver has packing that wipes the wireline as it moves and prevents oil, gas, and water from leaking around the wireline. A hose from the oil saver to the ground connects it to a grease gun that keeps push-ing grease into the lubricator to maintain the seal. High-pressure lubricators, over about 3,000 pounds per square inch (about 20 megapascals), include blow-out preventers so that a worker can bleed off pressure from the tubing or casing.

Unloading Gas Wells

Well servicing crews sometimes work on gas wells when salt water from the formation enters the tubing. Pressure of the water can prevent the gas from flowing out. The normal procedure in this case is to swab the brine out of the tubing in order to unload the well. Sometimes, a string of small-diameter tubing or coiled tubing is run into the well because the well can clean itself through small tubing better than through larger tubing.

8

FISHING

Oilfield workers have two names for pieces of metal lost or stuck in a well: *fish* and *junk*. A fish is a piece of equipment, pipe, or any other sizable piece of metal in the hole that should not be there. Junk is a smaller piece of metal, such as a broken bit tooth or a hand tool that a crew member dropped in the well accidentally. Junk can interfere with workover or well service operations. When it does, the operation ceases, and crew members have to fish (remove) the junk from the well. Similarly, a large piece of equipment, part of the tubing string, or any other large fish impedes work and must be removed.

The operation to recover a fish or junk is a fishing job. Fishing often involves rotating a tool in the hole or circulation of a workover fluid, so it may require a larger service rig.

However, many fishing operations can be done with wireline or coiled tubing run inside the production tubing.

TYPES OF FISH

Fish include drill pipe, drill collars, tubing, screen liners, packers, and sucker rods that are either stuck in the well or have broken off because of mechanical failure, corrosion, or abrasion.

Drill Pipe

Drill pipe or drill collars can get stuck in the hole for several reasons: (1) the hole can collapse around the pipe; (2) the pipe can get stuck in a keyseat, a small-diameter portion of the hole; or (3) pressure can hold the drill collars so securely to the wall of the hole that no amount of pulling can free the pipe.

The most common reason for the wall of the hole collapsing around the pipe is that, under certain conditions, salt water in pores of the rock can attract water in the drilling mud. If the formation consists of shale and the water in the mud is in contact with the water in the shale, the water in the mud has a tendency to transfer to the shale. Transferred water causes shale to expand; small sheets of shale then flake off into the hole, eventually fill it up, and the pipe sticks.

Pipe can also get stuck in a keyseat (fig. 8.1). A keyseat is caused by a dogleg, which is a severely crooked section of hole. ("It's as crooked as a dog's hind leg" is the expression that gives rise to the term.) The drill pipe tends to lean against the side of the dogleg and, as the pipe rotates, it digs out a new, smaller hole in the side of the main borehole.

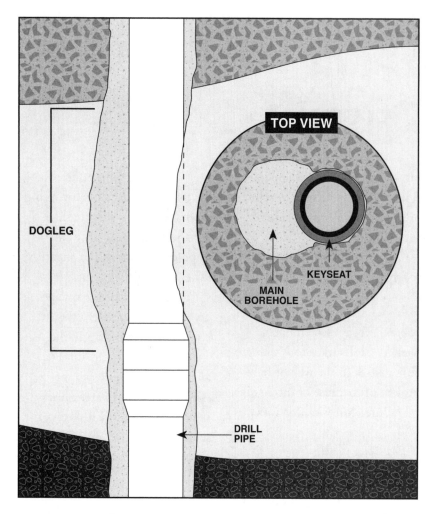

Figure 8.1. Drill pipe stuck in a keyseat

Tubing, Screen Liners, Packers, and Sucker Rods

Congealed drilling mud, sand in the annulus, a stuck packer, or a combination of these often sticks tubing in a hole.

Drilling mud often has a special clay in it that allows it to gel when it stops circulating. The gelled mud suspends the cuttings throughout the hole until drilling resumes so that they do not fall to the bottom. If not flushed out, congealed mud left over from drilling can trap both tubing and packers.

In a wire-wrapped screen completion (see Chap. 2), fine sand eventually infiltrates the gravel pack and the screen and fills up the inside of the slotted liner. When a workover crew comes in to clean out the sand, the tubing and screen liner may be stuck in the sand and gravel pack.

Sometimes debris from leftover drilling mud settles on top of packers and interferes with the slips, making it impossible to set or pull them.

Then, when the drill stem is pulled from the hole, the tool joint (the connector between joints) of the drill pipe or the wider drill collars can jam into the keyseat so hard that they cannot be freed by just pulling up.

Pipe can also stick in the hole when pressure within the wellbore is quite a bit higher than pressure in the formation. Higher pressure in the wellbore can cause a thick cake of solids to build up on the inside of the hole and trap the drill pipe. Also, when the drill stem is not rotating, the higher pressure can force the drill collars into the thick cake and stick them very firmly to the wall of the hole.

FISHING TOOLS AND ACCESSORIES

Fishing specialists have many tools available to them to retrieve fish from a well. Engineers have designed tools to grab fish and pull them up, tools to separate the stuck part of a drilling or tubing string from the part that is not stuck, tools to grind away whatever is wedging the fish, and tools to jar the fish out of the hole.

Spears and Overshots

Spears and overshots hold a stuck fish in place so that it does not fall to the bottom when it is freed and pull a fish out of the well. Both are run in on drill pipe, on tubing, or, in special designs, on coiled tubing. A spear (fig. 8.2) catches a hollow fish, such as tubing. Its diameter is smaller than the fish so that it fits inside it and grips it with slips.

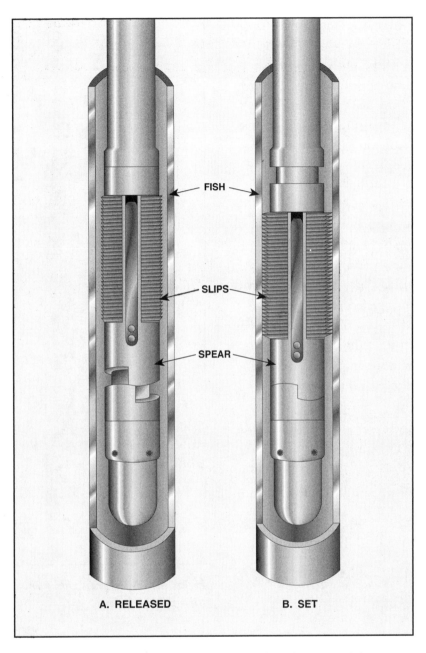

Figure 8.2. A spear goes inside the fish in a released position (A); once positioned, the spear is set and the fish removed (B).

An overshot fits over the outside of a fish and catches it by means of a grapple inside the overshot (fig. 8.3). The crew rotates and pulls up on the fishing string to set the grapple. It can catch a fish that is not hollow, such as a sucker rod, as well as a hollow fish.

The overshot is the more rugged tool because more metal can be built into its body than into a spear, which must fit inside a fish. Therefore, a service crew prefers to use an overshot whenever there is enough room for it. In the larger sizes, however, spears and overshots are about equal in strength.

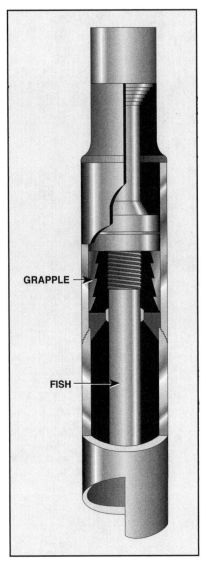

Figure 8.3. *An overshot fits over the outside of a fish.*

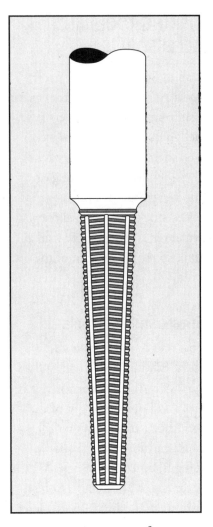

Figure 8.4. A taper tap forms screw threads inside a hollow fish.

Taper Taps and Die Collars

A tap is a tool for forming an internal, or female, screw thread. It consists of a hardened steel screw with longitudinal grooves that form cutting edges. The diameter of a taper tap decreases from the top to the end. (fig. 8.4).

Fishing crews run a taper tap into a hollow fish and rotate it to cut threads inside the fish. The tap grips the fish firmly and the crew can pull it out.

A die collar is the female counterpart of a taper tap (fig. 8.5). It fits over the outside of a fish to cut threads on it and grip it.

Taps and die collars cannot catch a fish that is free to turn because they use the resistance of the stuck fish to cut threads in it. They also cannot be unscrewed. The only way to release them is by breaking the tool or stripping the threads. The rig operator may, however, add a special tool called a safety joint above a tap or die collar. If the crew needs to disconnect the work string from the fish, the safety joint is designed to separate, allowing the crew to pull the work string out of the hole

and leaving in the hole the lower part of the safety joint, the joint of tubing below the safety joint, and the tap or die collar lodged in the fish.

Taps and die collars are used only when the clearance in the hole is too small to use a spear or overshot or if the extra gripping strength of a tap is needed.

Washover Pipe and Rotary Shoe

A washover string consists of several joints of washover pipe, which is similar to casing. Washover pipe, sometimes called washpipe, is small enough to fit inside the casing but large enough to fit outside the tubing (fig. 8.6). At the bottom of the washover pipe is a burn shoe, or rotary shoe. The rotary shoe is a hollow, cylindrical milling device that cuts on the inside, outside, and/or bottom. Different types of rotary shoes can drill out sand or shale in the annular space outside the fish, the sides of a metal fish that is stuck in the hole, junk on the bottom of the hole, or even rock and cement around the fish. The fishing specialist flushes out the drilled cuttings by circulating a fluid through the washpipe.

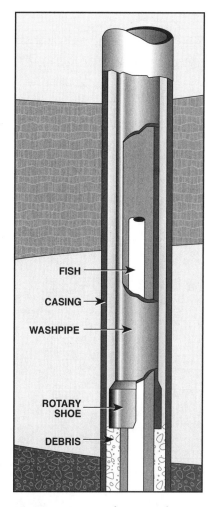

Figure 8.6. A washpipe with a rotary shoe on the bottom drills out the space around a fish.

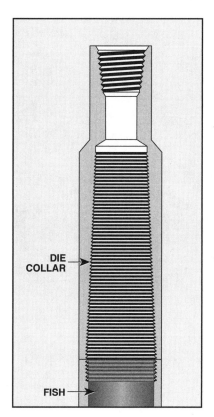

Figure 8.5. A die collar forms screw threads on the outside of a fish.

Mills

Mills are tools with, sharp, extremely hard cutting surfaces for removing metal, cement, sand, or scale by grinding or cutting while rotating. The crew runs them in on drill pipe or tubing to smooth off the top or enlarge an opening in a fish, grind up debris in the hole, clean out tubing, or ream out tight spots in the casing (fig. 8.7).

A junk mill grinds up junk in the hole. A packer mill works like a rotary shoe to cut out a packer. It includes a spear to catch the packer when it is freed or a junk basket (a special tool above the mill) to catch the milled pieces. A tapered mill reams out collapsed casing and removes burrs. Pilot mills and skirted mills have devices to guide them inside or over drill pipe or tubing. A pilot mill has an extension, or pilot, for this purpose. A skirted mill has a piece of metal shaped like a skirt to align it with the fish and keep it from rotating off.

Figure 8.7. Various types of mills remove metal, cement, sand, or scale.

Cutters

Cutters separate a section of drill pipe or tubing that is not stuck from the section that is. The fishing crew may use mechanical, jet, or chemical cutters.

Mechanical Cutters

Mechanical cutters work by rotating blades against a stuck fish. The blades are made of hardened steel. The two types of mechanical cutters are internal and external.

Internal cutters fit inside a hollow fish (fig. 8.8). They can be run in on sucker rods, regular or macaroni tubing, or drill pipe. After slips anchor the cutter inside the fish, a spring or a block pushes the knife assembly outward.

An external cutter fits over the outside of the fish to cut it (fig. 8.9). Part of the cutter is an overshot to pull the fish out after it is cut. Fishing crews usually run an external cutter in conjunction with a washover pipe and wash over a considerable length of the fish before making the cut. After washover, the crew ordinarily pulls out of the hole and puts the cutter on to cut and retrieve the free portion of the fish.

Both internal and external cutters may be hydraulically operated. In other words, pumping fluid down the hole rotates the knives.

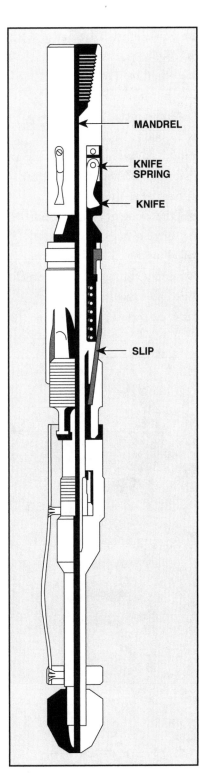

Figure 8.8. This internal cutter goes inside a fish to cut it when the cutter's knives are activated.

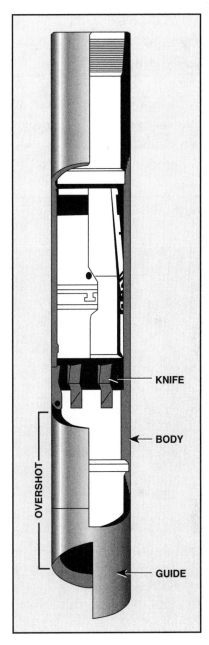

Figure 8.9. An external cutter goes over the outside of the fish; when activated, the knives cut the outside wall of the fish.

Jet and Chemical Cutters

A jet cutter (fig. 8.10) uses a shaped charge, similar to the charge in a perforating gun, which explodes outward in a thin line to cut the fish horizontally. Centralizers center the tool in the hole. Jet cutting leaves the pipe slightly flared at the cut (fig. 8.11), but this can be smoothed by a mill to allow an overshot to catch it.

A chemical cutter (fig. 8.12) uses a blast of acid to make a smooth cut with no flare or metal distortion. Although neither the jet nor the chemical cutter damages the string of casing or tubing surrounding the stuck pipe, coiled tubing specialists recommend that fishing crews cut stuck coiled tubing with a chemical cutter because a jet cutter can balloon the tubing out so much that it will be difficult to latch onto it with an overshot.

Jarring Tools

Bumper jars and mechanical jars jolt the fish either up or down to loosen it. They are usually run in on tubing or drill pipe, but sometimes on wireline.

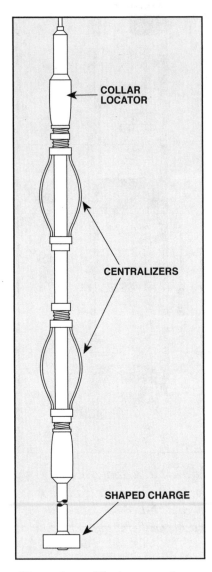

Figure 8.10. The jet cutter is lowered inside the fish. The shaped charge, when activated, cuts the fish.

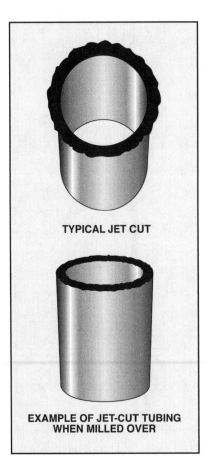

Figure 8.11. A jet cut flares the end of the fish.

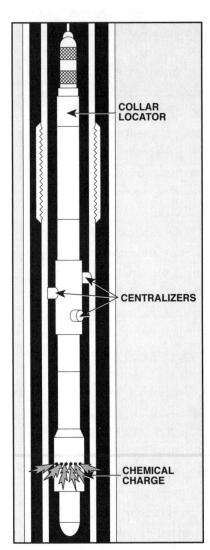

Figure 8.12. A chemical cutter blasts acid onto the fish to cut it.

Bumper Jars

A bumper jar (fig. 8.13) has two sections: an upper section, which moves up and down within a limited range, usually 12 to 36 inches (about 30 to 90 centimetres), and a lower section, which does not move. Raising the upper section with the fishing string to the limit of travel will produce a light upward jar on the lower section. Dropping the string quickly will produce a sharp downward jar, or bump, on the lower part. If the fish can be freed by a downward blow, a bumper jar can be very effective. The jarring blow will be stronger if the crew adds a few drill collars to the string just above the bumper jar for extra weight.

Mechanical Jars

When a powerful upward jar is needed to free a fish, the crew uses a mechanical jar. Two types of mechanical jars are rotary jars and hydraulic jars.

A rotary jar delivers an upward or downward impact by the sudden release of tripping devices inside the tool. It works by rotating the work string. The greater the torque, or turning force, the more intense the blow when the tool trips.

A hydraulic jar is a mandrel with a fluid and piston inside of it (fig. 8.14). As the crew raises the working string, the pull on

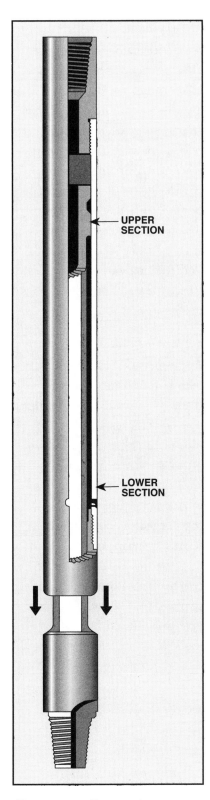

Figure 8.13. Bumper jar

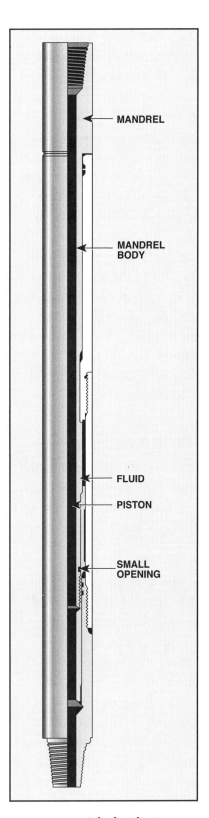

Figure 8.14. A hydraulic jar

the jar moves the fluid (usually oil) from one section to another through a small opening. The small opening forces the fluid to move slowly, which slows the stroke. The crew continues to pull up, stretching the working string while the jar opens. After the hydraulic delay, a release mechanism in the jar trips to allow the mandrel to spring up and deliver a sharp blow. The intensity of the blow depends on how much the crew stretches the string before the jar trips—the more stretch, the harder the blow. A few drill collars above the tool enhances the effect of both rotary and hydraulic jars.

Fishing Accessories

Adding a fishing accessory can make a fishing tool more effective, easier to use or retrieve, or can help find and identify a fish.

Safety Joint

A safety joint, as mentioned in the section on taper taps and die collars, is a special type of connector that is easy to disconnect. It consists of a short threaded piece of pipe that fits between a fishing tool and the work string. One type of safety joint has both threads and shear pins. If drill pipe, tubing, a taper tap, die collar, or washover pipe

connected to a safety joint gets stuck in the hole, the crew pulls up on the string. This breaks the safety joint's shear pins; rotating the string will then unscrew the safety joint and release the top of the string from the stuck section.

Most prudent rig operators will run a safety joint above an overshot or other fishing tool as a releasing device in case they cannot pull the fish or the releasing device in the fishing tool becomes inoperative. Many tools have safety joints built in at the factory.

Reversing Tool

The tool joints and couplings that connect joints of drill pipe or tubing ordinarily have right-handed threads. That is, they screw and unscrew in the same directions as ordinary household screws. A reversing tool converts right-handed torque to left-handed torque, so it reverses the direction of rotation. Sometimes when the crew needs to unscrew a connector from a fish, crew members risk unscrewing a joint of the fishing string instead of the tool attached to the fish. By using a reversing tool between the fishing string and the fishing tool, they can rotate the work string in the tightening direction while unscrewing the fishing tool.

Jar Accelerator

A jar accelerator increases the effectiveness of a hydraulic jar. It intensifies the jarring by using a spring or compressed gas that stores energy when the string is pulled up. It releases the energy when the hydraulic jar trips. An accelerator is useful in shallow wells where a short working string does not allow much stretch for the jar to work, and in directional or crooked holes, where the wall of the hole drags on the string.

Impression Block

An impression block is a block with lead or some other relatively soft coating on its bottom. The crew makes it up on drill pipe or tubing and sets it down on a fish. When they pull it back up, the soft material has a mirror-image impression of the top of the fish. The impression reveals the shape of the fish and its position in the hole—that is, whether it is centered or off to one side. This helps the crew determine the correct fishing tool.

Retrieving Junk

Junk subs and junk baskets are two types of junk retrievers. Both use circulating fluid to create areas of high and low pressure that direct the junk into a "basket." A crew can make them up on a working string above a bit or mill to catch the cuttings or run them in at the bottom of the string to pick up junk from the bottom of the hole. Some junk baskets have a shoe on the bottom that mills large pieces of junk into smaller pieces that can be recovered.

The fishing magnet uses a powerful magnet to pull up pieces of metal left on the bottom of a well. A magnet can only pick up a limited size and amount of junk, however.

FISHING TECHNIQUES

A service crew may have to try several techniques to remove a fish until they are successful.

Freeing Stuck Tubing or Drill Pipe

The first thing the crew will do to free stuck tubing or drill pipe is to pull up on it until it stretches tight and then turn on the circulating pump to apply pressure in the well. If the pipe appears to be stuck at or near the packer, crew members will try to unseat the packer to free the fish.

They will then try to jar the fish loose. If this does not work, they may spot oil down the hole (pump in a small amount of oil to lubricate the fish).

If none of these relatively easy procedures frees the fish, the crew tries one of several downhole methods. They may perforate the fish above the stuck area and circulate fluid to try to wash out the sand or mud holding it in the hole. To separate the free portion of a pipe from the stuck portion, they locate the exact point where it is stuck and either unscrew the connection above that point or cut the pipe. Finally, they may wash over the fish to drill out the obstruction.

Circulating and Perforating

To free a fish that is stuck by congealed drilling mud or sand, the crew first tries to wash out the mud or sand by circulation. Next, crew members may perforate the fish to allow the fluid to circulate better through it by making several holes at varying levels to allow the fluid to circulate progressively deeper. As the circulating fluid becomes clear at the surface, indicating that the congealed mud or sand in the annulus has circulated out, the crew pulls on the fish to see if it is free.

Free-Point Indicator

To determine exactly where pipe or tubing is stuck, a fishing crew uses a free-point indicator. Crew members run the free-point indicator inside tubing, casing, or drill pipe on a conductor line and switch it on. The indicator sends electrical impulses through the pipe. The pipe relays them to a detector on the surface. As the crew lowers the switched-on indicator, they twist or pull up on the stuck pipe to put tension on it. The indicator detects microscopic movement in the stretched pipe when the indicator is above the point where the pipe is stuck (the freeze point). When crew members move the indicator below the freeze point, the microscopic movement stops. They note the length of conductor line run in to determine the approximate depth of the fish. They can then raise and lower the indicator to find the exact freeze point.

This method is very accurate and reliable, giving good, consistent results.

String Shot

A string shot is used to unscrew, or back off, the connection between two joints of drill pipe or tubing. The crew often runs in the string-shot assembly (fig. 8.15) with the free-point detector. The actual shot is a length of Primacord explosive.

The crew places the assembly so that the string shot is opposite the coupling or tool joint they want to back off. Then they apply torque, or turning force, to the stuck string of pipe in the unscrewing direction. While maintaining torque, they detonate the explosion. The explosion, if placed correctly, breaks out the threads. It works like tapping a pickle jar on the counter to loosen the cap. Sometimes the crew needs to use several shots to loosen the coupling.

String shots do not damage the pipe that is free above the freeze point. String shot assemblies can be as small as ¾ inch (19 millimetres) in diameter.

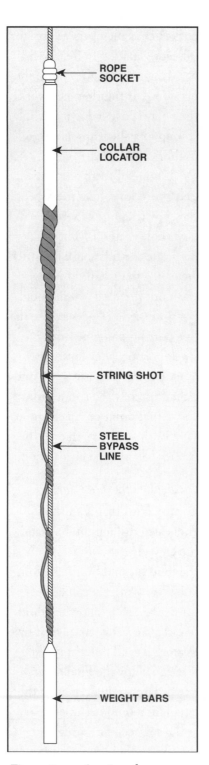

Figure 8.15. A string-shot assembly breaks out threads to back off a joint that is not stuck from one that is.

Washover

If the outside of the fish is stuck, the crew washes over the fish to free it and catches it with an overshot. Crew members then use a string shot to back off the newly freed joint from those below it.

If the inside of the fish is plugged, the crew may not be able to run a string shot to back off the fish when the washover is completed. In this case, crew members put an external cutter on the lower end of the washover pipe to make an outside cut on the fish.

The washover assembly also usually includes jars, bumper subs, and safety joints above the washover pipe.

Cutting

Until the advent of the string-shot technique, internal cutting was the best way to loosen stuck drill pipe or tubing. String-shot back-off has almost completely replaced internal cutting, but cutting is still used to recover large-size casing.

REMOVING A STUCK PACKER

To remove a permanent packer, the service crew simply drills it out with a packer mill and lets the pieces fall to the bottom of the hole or into a junk basket. When a retrievable packer sticks, either because its releasing mechanism has failed or because it has sanded up or corroded, the crew has several means of getting it out. First, crew members back off the tubing above the packer. Then they may be able to jar the packer out with a hydraulic jar. Sometimes they fire a string shot across the packer to produce a jar to release the slips. If jarring alone does not work, they may drill out the seals and slips with a washover pipe and rotary shoe or with a mill. They then jar the drilled packer and pull it out with an overshot or spear.

FISHING PARTED SUCKER RODS

When the sucker rod string breaks, the repair crew pulls the top part of the string out of the well, removes the broken rod, and runs a fishing tool to recover the lower portion of the string. The service crew can often reuse undamaged sucker rods after retrieving the broken section.

RETRIEVING A SCREEN LINER

Screen liners stick because of sand inside both the slotted liner and the screen and gravel pack around it. After removing the production tubing, the fishing crew circulates fluid into the liner and washes the sand out of the slotted liner and screen.

Then crew members run in a spear assembly, including jars, to pull the liner out while continuing to circulate fluid. If the screen liner is still stuck, they drill out its centralizers with washover pipe. When the centralizers are gone, the liner can usually be jarred out of the hole.

9

SAND CLEANOUT AND WORKOVER

Workover jobs may include cleaning sand out of the well and adding a means of preventing sand from entering it, replacing liners, plugging the well, repairing casing, drilling deeper, and drilling around obstructions in the well. Some workover jobs require only a wireline to lower tools, but others need to rotate tubing or drill pipe, so the workover rig has equipment to rotate the pipe string. Operations that need to circulate workover fluid into the well require pumps and storage tanks.

SAND CLEANOUT

In a wire-wrapped screen completion, fine sand eventually infiltrates the gravel pack and the screen and fills up the inside of the slotted liner. Sometimes, however, in spite of every attempt to exclude it, sand enters the well and causes trouble. When this happens, a workover crew cleans the well out.

The method of cleaning out the sand depends on where the sand is and how tightly it is packed. All methods use circulation of a fluid, usually salt water, to flush the sand out.

Using a Macaroni Rig or Coiled Tubing

One method uses either a macaroni rig (fig. 9.1) or coiled tubing (fig. 9.2). A macaroni rig is a relatively small rig that handles special lightweight, small-diameter pipe called macaroni. The crew leaves the production tubing and packers in place and lowers the macaroni string or coiled tubing, generally about 1 to 1¼ inches (about 25–30 mm) in diameter, inside the production tubing. Crew members lower the string until it just reaches the top of the sand. Then they circulate salt water down the tubing at a high velocity, lowering the string as the sand washes out. This high-velocity salt water forces the sand to the surface through the annulus between the production tubing and the macaroni or coiled tubing.

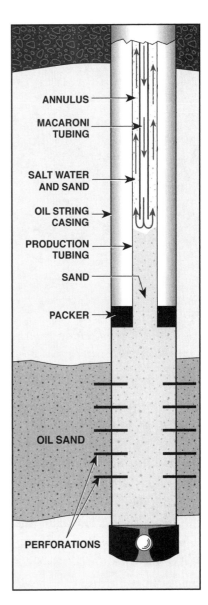

ANNULUS
MACARONI TUBING
SALT WATER AND SAND
OIL STRING CASING
PRODUCTION TUBING
SAND
PACKER
OIL SAND
PERFORATIONS

Figure 9.1. Macaroni tubing fits inside the production tubing to wash sand out.

99

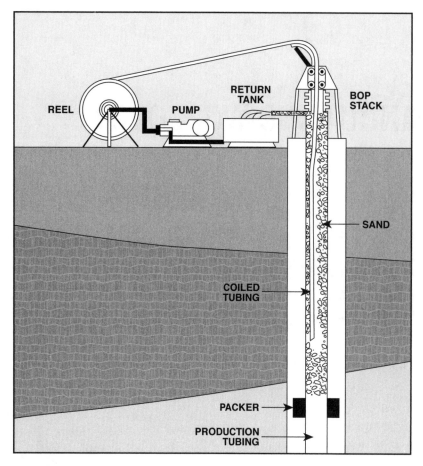

Figure 9.2. Coiled tubing washes sand up the annulus between production tubing and coiled tubing.

Less common is reverse circulation. In reverse circulation, salt water is pumped down the annulus and returns up the macaroni or coiled tubing. This is used if the fluid velocity in the annulus is too low to lift the sand out of the well. Because the inside diameter of the tubing is smaller than the casing diameter, the pressure is higher there. A disadvantage of reverse circulation is that the pressure of the salt water against the outside of coiled tubing can collapse it.

A macaroni rig is particularly useful for sand cleanout from a barge or offshore platform because the hoist and working string are lightweight.

Circulating through Production Tubing

If a macaroni rig or coiled tubing equipment is not available or there is an obstruction in the tubing, the crew pulls the production tubing and packer out of the well. Crew members then run the tubing back into the well and clean out the sand by reverse circulation through the tubing (fig. 9.3). After they finish, they reset the packer.

Using Washover Pipe

In some cases, the sand gets packed solidly in the annulus between the tubing and the casing. Sand can enter the annulus through a hole in the casing or through the perforations. The tubing gets stuck when this happens, preventing the crew from pulling it for service or workover jobs.

To clean out the sand in the tubing-casing annulus and unstick the tubing, the workover crew first backs off or cuts the free portion of the tubing above the sand and pulls it out. Then crew members use a washover string that reaches from the surface all the way down to the packed sand (fig. 9.4). As the rotary (washover) shoe mills out the sand, circulation washes it up the annulus.

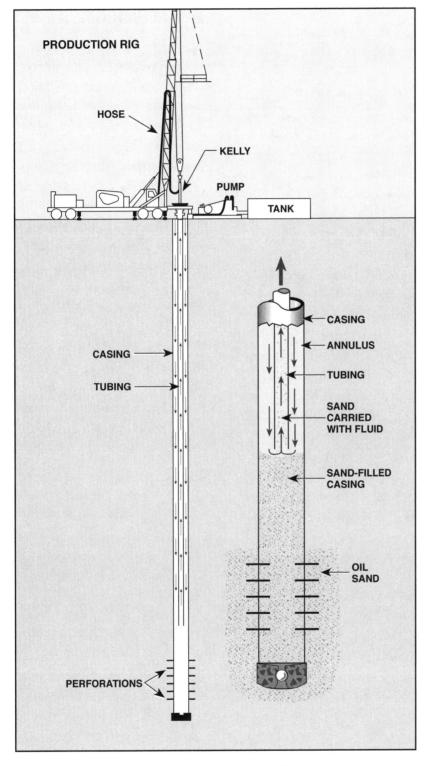

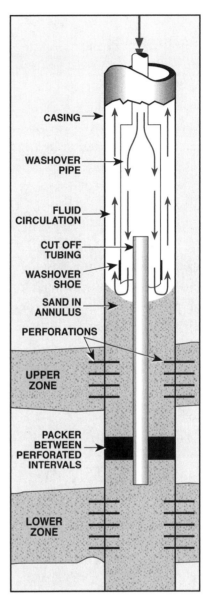

Figure 9.4. A washover pipe mills out packed sand around the tubing.

Figure 9.3. Sand is washed up the tubing when fluid is pumped down the casing-tubing annulus.

Removing a Screen Liner

A well that was completed with a screen liner may need repair after a time. As more and more sand passes into the slotted liner, the cutting action of the sand grains gradually enlarges the slots. Eventually, a workover crew must remove the damaged liner, by pulling the tubing, or by cutting and fishing it if it is stuck. After removing the liner, crew members usually must clean out the well to the bottom of the open hole in order to condition the hole for the new liner. They use drill pipe or tubing and a small drill bit for this job.

Equipment

The type of job and the manner of cleanout determine what size rig and what equipment layout the contractor brings to the job. A macaroni rig need be no heavier than a well servicing unit suitable for sucker rods, but it does need a storage tank and high-pressure pump to circulate salt water.

A larger and heavier workover rig will be needed to unseat the packers and pull tubing. The pump needs to move a lot of fluid but at a lower pressure than the pump on a macaroni or coiled tubing rig. Moderate-depth cleanouts can be performed with a spudder handling the pipe in singles. If numerous round trips might be needed, a doubles rig will enable faster trips.

Finally, when the crew has to run washover pipe, the rig's mast and hoist must be large enough to handle the extra weight of the washover pipe. A washover string is generally several times heavier than an equivalent length of tubing because of its larger diameter. The pump needs to be about the same size as the pump on a rig running plain tubing. Since washover involves rotating the work string, the rig includes a top drive, power sub, or rotary.

Whenever a sand-filled fluid is pumped out of the well, it goes into a tank, where the sand settles out and the fluid is reused.

SAND CONTROL

A company representative may call in a workover company to control sand in existing wells because A) the original completion was inadequate, B) a crew has drilled the well deeper to a new formation that produces sand, or C) the characteristics of the reservoir have changed.

Adding a gravel pack is the most common method of controlling sand in an existing well. Adding a gravel pack as a workover job is no different from installing it during completion.

Another method is to bond the sand grains using a plastic or a resin to "lock" them in place. This is known as chemical consolidation. A third method places a resin-coated sand pack.

Chemical Consolidation

In chemical consolidation, also called plastic squeezing, the crew pumps a resin that mixes with the sand in the formation (fig. 9.5). In a second stage, crew members pump in a hardener. The resin and hardener mixture, like epoxy glue, causes the grains to stick together. In the last stage, the crew pumps in a chemical that washes away excess resin so that the formation remains porous and permeable enough for the oil or gas to flow.

Chemical consolidation is probably the least-effective means of sand control, but it has some advantages. For one, it leaves no sand or equipment in the hole, which makes future maintenance easier. The treatment is simple and needs a minimum of surface equipment. The crew need not pull the production tubing or kill the well and uses retrievable packers to isolate the area to be treated. Finally, crew members can then clean out any loose sand in the upper zones of a multizone completion. Its main disadvantage is that the chemicals used evaporate easily, and the fumes are a hazard to workers.

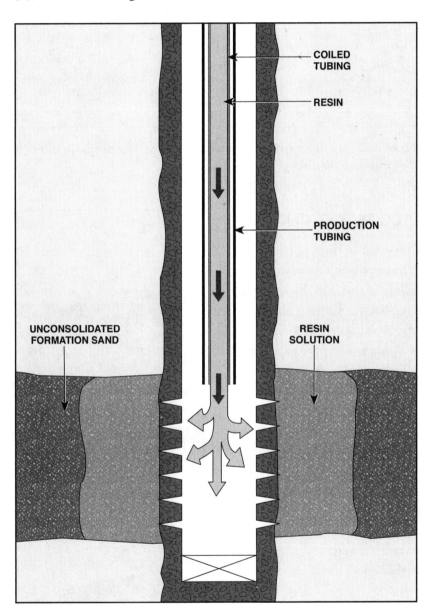

Figure 9.5. Chemical consolidation uses a resin that glues the formation's sand grains together when it hardens.

Resin-Coated Sand Packs

To form a resin-coated sand pack, the workover crew begins with a slurry (a solid suspended in a liquid) of sand and a resin. The crew pumps the slurry down the production tubing or coiled tubing into the casing and its perforations. When the resin hardens, it forms a plug that oil and gas, but not sand, can flow through. To improve the flow through the pack, the crew often drills a small hole into the resin, using a downhole mud motor and a small bit (fig. 9.6 A, B, C).

Resin-coated sand packs have many of the advantages of gravel packs without leaving screen and junk in the well to interfere with future service. They are sometimes ideal for repairing gravel packs that have failed. However, they may leave voids if more resin squeezes through some perforations than others.

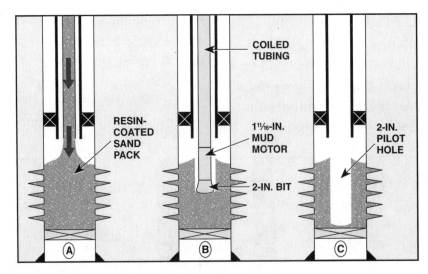

Figure 9.6. To form a resin-coated sand pack, the crew pumps in resin slurry, then drills through it after it hardens.

PLUG-BACK CEMENTING

Plug-back cementing places a cement plug at one or more points in a well to shut off flow. Plug-back cementing is most often used to isolate a lower zone from the upper part of the well (fig. 9.7), usually because the lower zone is depleted of oil and gas. The cement plug shuts off the lower part of the formation so that only the higher area produces. The plug keeps produced fluids from migrating down into the lower zone. It also prevents salt water in the lower zone from migrating to the higher one.

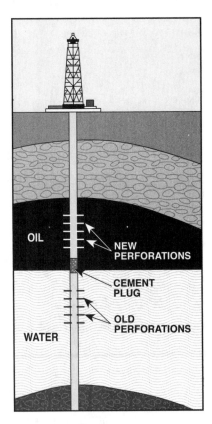

Figure 9.7. One reason to place a cement plug is to shut off a lower producing zone in order to produce a formation nearer the surface.

Plugging back may also be used to seal off a dry well before abandoning it or when preparing to sidetrack. Sidetracking is drilling a new hole to bypass something that is permanently stuck in the hole (see fig. 9.19). The workover crew places the plug at the depth where they will start the sidetrack. Then it starts drilling toward one side, and the plug seals off the old hole.

Placing a Plug Using Tubing

Workover crews can use one of two methods to place a cement plug. In one, they place a mechanical plug at the depth they want the bottom of the cement plug to be (fig. 9.8A). Then they pump cement down drill pipe or tubing, pushing the cement down the pipe with another fluid (fig. 9.8B).

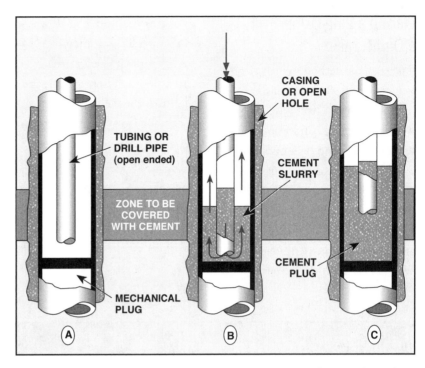

Figure 9.8. Cement is pumped down the production tubing and up the annulus to form a cement plug.

They keep pumping until the level of cement outside the tubing or pipe is equal to the level inside the tubing or pipe. When the levels are the same, they stop pumping and slowly pull the tubing or pipe out of the cement, just above the top of the cement plug (fig. 9.8C). Finally, they pump out the extra cement left in the pipe or tubing by reverse circulation, leaving the cement plug in place.

Placing a Plug Using a Dump Bailer

The second method, which works best in shallow wells, involves a dump bailer and a mechanical plug run in on a wireline. A dump bailer is a long cylinder that holds cement (fig. 9.9). Its diameter is small enough to fit inside casing. The bailer has a spring mechanism that opens it and dumps the cement when the crew pulls up on the wireline.

In this method, the crew sets the mechanical plug—a basket—in the well at the desired depth. Then, it runs the bailer into the well and dumps the cement from the bailer onto the basket. The cement plug forms on top of the mechanical plug. This method requires only a small amount of cement, and the crew can usually place the plug at an exact spot in the well.

CASING AND LINER REPAIR

Casing and liners have the same problems and are repaired in the same ways. In this section, wherever the term casing is used, it generally means liners as well.

Corrosion, abrasion, pressure, and other destructive forces can create holes or splits in the casing. One way that workover crew members know that the casing has a hole is when they find shale or sand inside the well after pulling the tubing.

If they suspect a hole in the casing, workover crew members can locate it by running a packer on the production tubing. They set the packer at various depths and apply pressure to the annulus between the tubing and the casing by pumping in a fluid, usually brine. Each time, they wait several minutes and watch the annular pressure. As long as the packer is above the hole, the pressure does not decline. If the packer is below the hole, however, annular pressure bleeds off into the formation through the hole. They must repair the hole to maintain good production. Squeeze cementing is one way of repairing holes in casing. Other methods are patching it with a liner patch, replacing part of the string, or running a liner to cover the bad place in the casing string.

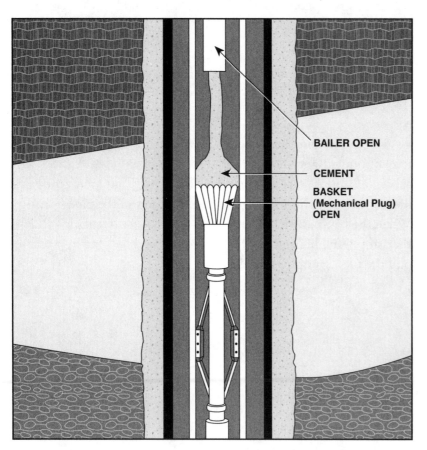

BAILER OPEN

CEMENT

BASKET (Mechanical Plug) OPEN

Figure 9.9. With basket (mechanical plug) open, the bailer dumps cement on top of the basket to form a plug.

Squeeze Cementing

In squeeze cementing the crew pumps cement down drill pipe or tubing to an opening in a well's casing and applies pressure (fig. 9.10A and B). A tool on the end of the drill pipe or tubing called a cement retainer prevents the cement from flowing up the annulus. The pumping pressure forces the cement into the openings (perforations in this case) in the casing and against the formation behind it. The opening may be a hole that is the result of damage to the casing or an intentionally created hole, such as perforations. Workover crews can also squeeze cement against a part of the hole with no casing (as in an open-hole completion).

Squeeze cementing, like plug-back cementing, is useful for sealing off water in a lower zone from the oil in a higher zone as the water level rises (fig. 9.10C and D).

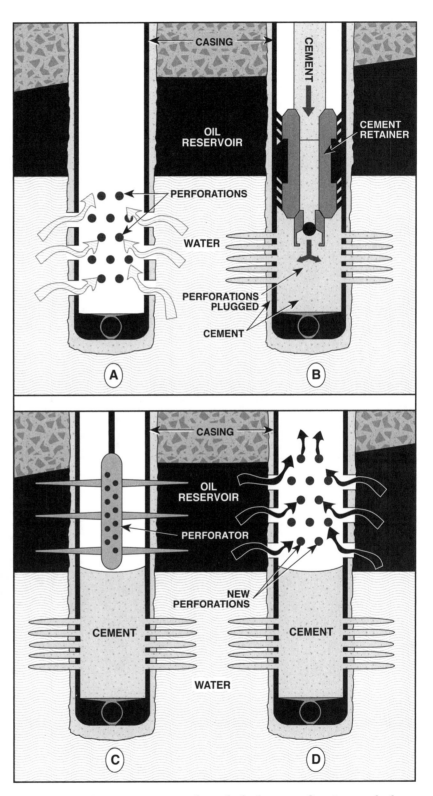

Figure 9.10. Squeezing cement through the lower perforations seals them (A, B). Then, the upper part of the zone is perforated (C, D).

Other uses are to repair holes in the casing; to fill empty spots, or channels, behind casing where cement should be located but for some reason is not; and to seal off an upper depleted zone when the lease operator wishes to produce the well from a lower zone (fig. 9.11).

The usual squeeze cementing techniques are the bradenhead squeeze and the packer squeeze. In both of these methods, the crew usually places a cement or mechanical plug inside the casing below the area to be squeezed and pressure-tests the tubing and casing for weak spots or leaks.

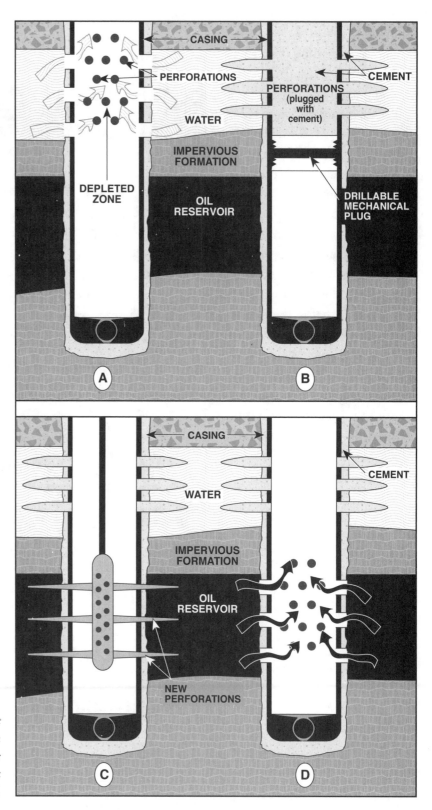

Figure 9.11. Squeezing cement through perforations next to an upper producing zone that has been depleted seals it off so that a lower zone can be perforated.

Bradenhead Squeeze

In a bradenhead squeeze job, the crew places a cement plug just below the squeeze point—that is, below the casing hole or perforations they want to plug (fig. 9.12). Next, crew members run tubing, drill pipe, or coiled tubing to the depth of the squeeze and pump cement through the pipe. The cement leaves the pipe near the squeeze point and displaces well fluids up the annulus. When enough cement has been placed, crew members pump a workover fluid down the tubing after it.

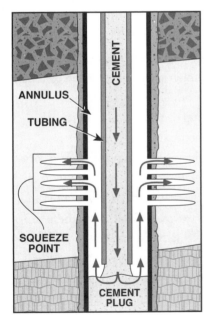

Figure 9.12. In a bradenhead squeeze, the casinghead is closed to allow hydraulic pressure to squeeze cement into the hole or perforations in the casing.

They then pull the tubing or drill pipe string above the squeeze point and seal off the annulus by closing a valve on the casinghead (formerly called the bradenhead). This maintains the pressure in the well. Slowly more pressure is applied through the tubing or drill pipe by pumping in more fluid. The hydraulic pressure forces the cement to move through the hole or perforations in the casing because the sealed wellhead prevents it from going anywhere else.

It works like shutting off the end of a hose that has a leak in it and then turning the faucet on. When the hose fills with water, pressure from the open faucet forces the water out the only available hole. After the squeeze, a crew may remove any remaining cement from the well by reversing the flow of circulating fluid, but usually crew members leave the cement in place and drill it out after it hardens.

Packer Squeeze

The technique for packer squeezing is almost the same as described for a bradenhead squeeze. The only difference is that the crew sets a special packer to seal off the annulus near the squeeze depth instead of closing the well at the casinghead (fig. 9.13). The packer sits above the squeeze point and isolates it from the surface.

The packer method allows a higher hydraulic pressure than is usually possible on a bradenhead squeeze; higher pressure pushes more cement into the hole. Using a packer also makes controlling the amount and location of the cement easier because the packer isolates the zone to be treated.

A permanent or a retrievable packer may be used in the packer squeeze method. The usual permanent packer is called a cement retainer, and the crew can set it with tubing or on a wireline. A retrievable squeeze packer is similar to a retrievable production packer, but the workover crew can reuse it many times without damaging its resilient sealing element.

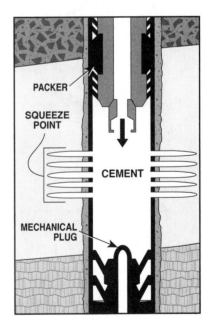

Figure 9.13. A packer seals off the annulus so that hydraulic pressure squeezes cement into holes or perforations.

Liner Patch

A liner patch is a thin-walled corrugated steel tube that patches a hole in casing or liner (fig. 9.14). Corrugation reduces the diameter so that it will fit inside the casing. To install a liner patch, first crew members scrape the wall of the casing to remove rust and scale where they will make the repair. They then glue a layer of fiberglass mat on the outside of the patch using an epoxy resin (similar to epoxy glue). Just before lowering the patch into the well, they apply additional epoxy resin to the outside of the fiberglass. They then run the patch to the correct depth to place the liner patch next to the hole in the casing. Finally, they expand the tube to flatten out the corrugations and fit tightly against the inside of the casing to patch the hole. This process reduces the diameter of the borehole in that spot slightly, but not enough to prevent the passage of most tools.

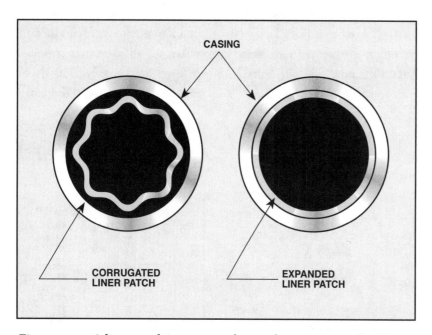

Figure 9.14. A liner patch is corrugated so its diameter is smaller than the casing diameter. After it is in place, it is flattened against the casing and glued.

Replacing Casing

Sometimes casing develops a hole near the surface. If the casing is not cemented or stuck, the crew can cut the string below the hole and pull the damaged part out. On the bottom of the new casing string, crew members attach a casing patch to connect it to the top of the old casing or tubing. The casing patch is a large-diameter tool that uses a synthetic rubber or lead seal to grip the outside of the casing or tubing, like an overshot. The casing patch then becomes a permanent part of the string.

Adding a Liner

If the crew cannot pull the upper part of the casing or repair a hole in it by squeeze cementing or using a liner patch, the company representative may decide to set and cement a complete string of pipe as a liner all the way to the surface. This will salvage the well, but production capacity may be lower than with the original casing and tubing because of the smaller diameter of the liner.

Opening Collapsed Casing

Sometimes casing partially or completely collapses because of corrosion or earth movement. Dents or scrape marks on the tubing after a workover crew pulls it from the well indicate that the casing has collapsed. Often these marks indicate the exact depth at which the collapse occurred.

If casing or tubing in the lower part of the wellbore has collapsed or buckled, and if the upper part of the string appears to be in good condition, the workover crew can use a casing roller or swage to open up the pipe. A casing roller has several heavy-duty rollers mounted on a mandrel (fig. 9.15). The crew runs it down tubing or drill pipe to the depth of the deformed casing and rotates it slowly. As the rollers contact all sides of the casing, they restore it to roughly its original diameter and roundness.

A swage can be used for tubing or casing. It is a blunt-nosed metal cylinder that the crew lifts and lets fall while rotating it to pound the collapsed section open (fig. 9.16).

If collapsed casing does not open up with either of these tools, the crew may need to side-track.

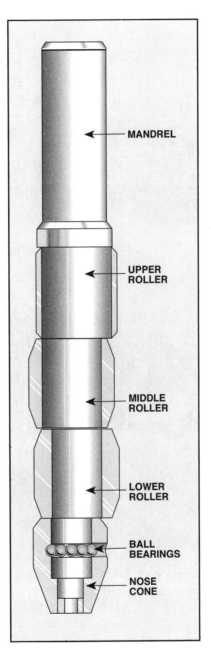

Figure 9.15. *Casing roller*

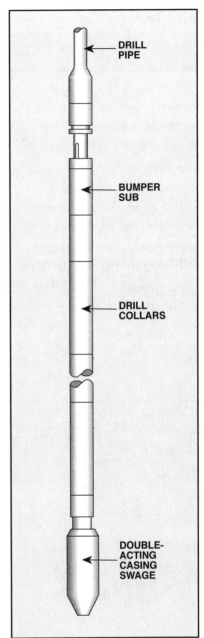

Figure 9.16. Casing swage

SIDETRACKING

Usually, workover and drilling crews try to drill holes as vertically as possible. Sometimes, however, they need to drill on a slant, which is called directional drilling. Sidetracking is the workover term for drilling a directional hole in order to bypass an obstruction in the well that crew members cannot remove, such as a fish or junk, or damage in the well that they cannot repair, such as collapsed casing (fig. 9.17). They may also sidetrack in order to deepen a well.

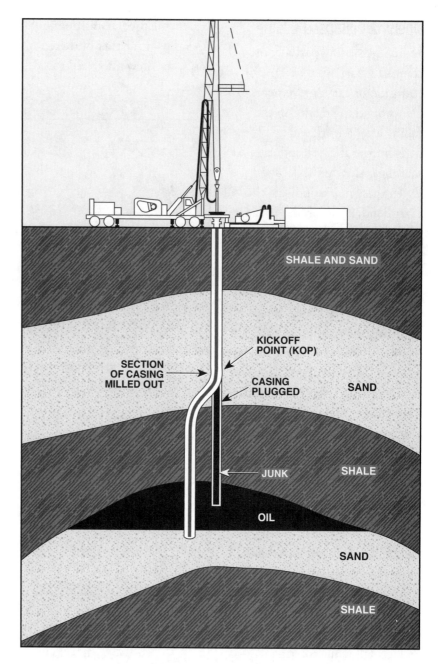

Figure 9.17.   Sidetracking drills around a fish that cannot be removed or other unrepairable damage.

Crews drill directional holes for many other reasons besides sidetracking. One is to place the bottom of a well at a better location to drain the reservoir. Offshore, where space is limited, they often drill a large number of directional wells (as many as twenty) from a single relatively small platform to exploit a reservoir that may cover several acres.

Occasionally, oil and gas are located in vertical, rather than horizontal, fractures (fig 9.18). When this happens, the driller can even drill a hole that turns completely sideways, or horizontally, so that the wellbore passes through several vertical fractures to drain them.

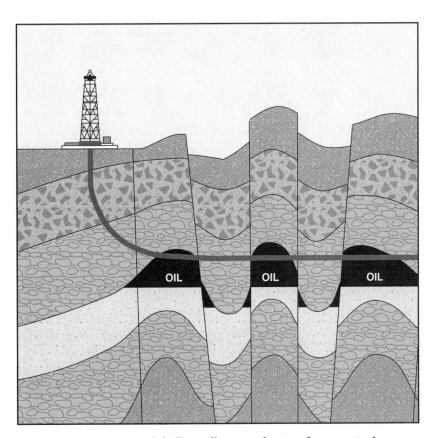

Figure 9.18. Horizontal drilling allows production from vertical reservoirs next to each other.

Method and Equipment

To sidetrack, the workover crew first makes a "window" in the casing above the obstruction to start the sidetrack hole. For this, crew members use a mill run on drill pipe or tubing (fig. 9.19A). Next, they plug back the wellbore with cement (fig. 9.19B). Finally, they make up a drill string with special tools, such as a whipstock, bent housing, or bent sub, that slant the drill bit a few degrees off vertical (fig. 9.19C).

A whipstock is a long steel tool whose bottom end anchors to the cement plug (fig. 9.20). One side of the whipstock is straight and rests against the side of the hole. The other side tapers to direct the drill stem away from the vertical. A bent sub is an attachment for the bottom of the drill stem that deflects a downhole motor slightly off vertical. The downhole motor is at the bottom of the drill string just above the bit. It works hydraulically when fluid is circulated and turns the bit without having to rotate the drill stem, which would be impossible in a curved wellbore. A bent housing is a housing for the downhole motor that deflects it off vertical.

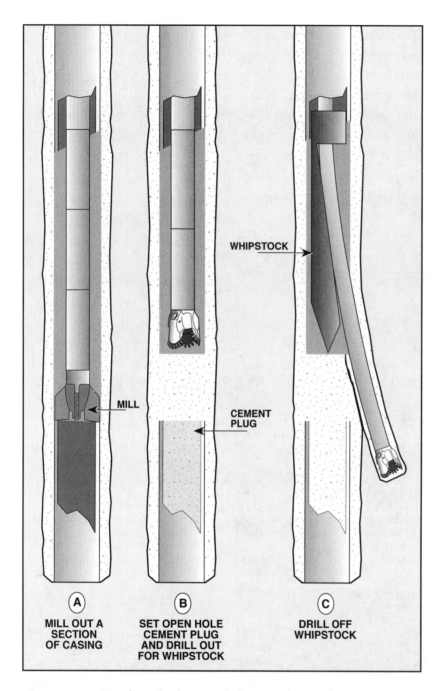

A MILL OUT A SECTION OF CASING

MILL

B SET OPEN HOLE CEMENT PLUG AND DRILL OUT FOR WHIPSTOCK

WHIPSTOCK

CEMENT PLUG

C DRILL OFF WHIPSTOCK

Figure 9.19.   To sidetrack, the crew drills a window in the casing, sets a cement plug, and drills ahead with a whipstock and downhole motor. The whipstock is tapered to direct the drill string a few degrees off vertical.

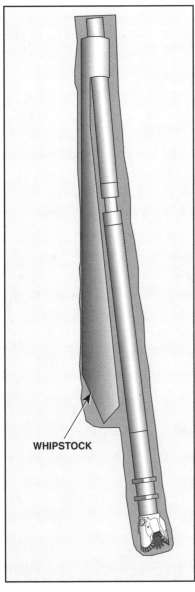

Figure 9.20. Whipstock

These tools put a bend of 1 to 3 degrees in the drill string. The directional hole will bend no more than 2 degrees per 100 feet (30 metres) of depth, so it only gradually angles away from the vertical. Directional drillers make frequent surveys to determine the distance and direction that the bit has drilled. They adjust the slant by changing, for example, the amount of weight on the bit and the speed of rotation.

When the crew reaches the new bottom of the well, they complete it by setting a liner.

DRILLING DEEPER

Sometimes, the operating company hires a workover crew to clean out the casing and drill the well deeper. One reason to drill deeper is to locate another producing zone below the depleted original producing zone.

Or, when sand clogs a screen liner, the crew may remove the bad liner and deepen the well rather than replace the liner.

Method and Equipment

Before drilling deeper, the workover crew must be sure that the casing can contain the pressure of the drilling mud. Crew members squeeze cement into the perforations and pressure-test the casing to make sure that it will hold.

Next, they rig up a heavy-duty workover rig, which is really a light-duty drilling rig. Deepening the hole requires the same type of auxiliary equipment that the original drilling crew used: mud circulating pumps, mud tanks, mud mixing facilities, and a prime mover. Usually drilling deeper goes on 24 hours a day, so the crew will include enough workers to rotate shifts. The contractor may run the drill bit into the well either on drill pipe or on tubing. Drilling deeper with coiled tubing is still in the developmental stage, but may someday be an option.

After drilling out the casing shoe at the bottom of the casing string and applying pressure to the open hole to test the squeeze-cementing job once again, drilling deeper is basically the same as drilling a new well. One difference is that a workover crew often reverses circulation of the drilling mud (fig. 9.21). In reverse circulation, mud travels to the surface through the small-diameter tubing, which requires less force than pumping mud up the larger casing. This allows the use of smaller pumps and lighter rotating equipment, so the company representative can contract for a workover rig rather than a drilling rig.

There is, however, extra danger of a blowout. The weight of the drilling mud usually overcomes formation pressure, so crew members must pay strict attention to keeping the hole full of mud while tripping in and out and watching the level in the mud tanks. They also use blowout preventers on the rig.

After the deeper hole is finished, the company representative usually hires a logging crew to test the formation exposed by the new wellbore. If enough hydrocarbons are present, the crew completes the new section by setting and perforating a new liner or casing.

Figure 9.21. In reverse circulation, the mud is pumped down the annulus and up the tubing.

10

WELL STIMULATION

Well stimulation includes techniques for overcoming the problem of a tight formation, or one that has a low permeability. Remember that permeability is a measure of how well the pores that contain hydrocarbons are connected to each other. Extracting the hydrocarbons from tight reservoirs is difficult and slow. On the other hand, the natural permeability of the rock may be adequate, but the formation near the wellbore may be damaged in a way that restricts the flow channels in porous rock. Formation damage can occur during drilling, completion, workover, production, or injection.

Low permeability, whether natural or artificial, reduces productivity to a rate that is not economical. Well stimulation is successful enough that many wells are stimulated immediately after completion and then whenever production drops because of low permeability.

Well stimulation overcomes low permeability by creating new flow channels or enlarging old ones. There are three ways to do this. The oldest method is to use explosives. During the 1930s, acid stimulation, or acidizing, became commercially available. Hydraulic fracturing, the third stimulation method, was introduced in 1948.

EXPLOSIVES

As early as the 1860s, crews exploded nitroglycerin inside wells to improve their productivity. They simply lowered a nitro charge into the open hole on a conductor line and detonated it to fracture the formation. Nitro shooting was fairly routine until the advent of acidizing and hydraulic fracturing.

For a time in the 1960s, lease operators experimented with nuclear explosives in a limited number of gas wells. While this method increased production somewhat, the cost was prohibitive.

Oil companies are still interested in explosive techniques because certain kinds of tight formations do not respond readily to either acidizing or hydraulic fracturing. Research continues in an effort to find other techniques that might increase production, but fracturing and acidizing are currently the most effective well stimulation methods.

Figure 10.1.   Several powerful, truck-mounted pumps are arranged at the well site for a fracturing job.

HYDRAULIC FRACTURING

Hydraulic fracturing is all about pressure. It works on the same principle as squeeze cementing. Several powerful pumps (fig. 10.1) inject a liquid, the fracturing fluid, into the well at a fast rate. The fluid develops a high pressure, which actually splits, or fractures, the rock. To visualize this, imagine splitting a log with an ax. The ax head is a wedge. A wedge first cuts a tiny crack in the log that the force of the blow enlarges into a wider cut until the log splits. In fracturing, the fluid acts as a wedge and its high pressure is the force that pushes it into the rock. Hydraulic fracturing splits the rock instead of the casing because the casing is stronger than the rock.

Hydraulic fracturing improves the productivity of a well by either creating new fractures that act as flow channels or extending existing flow channels farther into the formation. Fracturing is a usual part of completion, and refracturing to restore productivity of an old well is a regular procedure. Workover people commonly shorten the word fracturing to *frac*, as in frac job and frac unit.

Fracturing Fluid

Fracturing fluid may be either oil-based or water-based. In reality, the fluid is nearly always brine because it is safe, available, and cheap. Additives adjust the fluid's properties for various formations and conditions. One additive prevents the water from reacting with clays in the formation. Additives may also adjust the viscosity of the fluid. Viscosity is how thick a liquid is; for example, oil is more viscous than water. Some fracturing fluids are gels, which suspend the proppants better. Polymer additives reduce friction between the fluid and the walls of the tubing. Although this may not sound as if it would be a factor, any slowing of the fluid due to friction necessitates larger pumps to keep the injection rate high enough. Finally, additives reduce fluid loss into the formation.

Fluid loss is the process whereby fracturing fluid soaks into the rock. Although the permeability of a well requiring fracturing is considered too low for economical production, it is not so low that the fracturing fluid cannot permeate the pores. Fluid loss is important in hydraulic fracturing because it controls the length of the fracture. The more the fluid permeates the formation (high fluid loss), the shorter the fracture will be because the pressure disperses along with the fluid (fig. 10.2). Since long fractures are best, low fluid loss is more desirable.

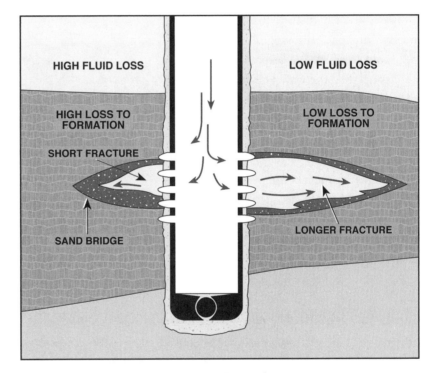

Figure 10.2. High fluid loss creates shorter fractures.

Propping Agents

Fracturing fluid must not only break down the formation but also transport proppants, or propping agents, into the fracture. Proppants hold open the fractures when fracturing is complete. They are needed because when the crew stops pumping, the hydraulic pressure dissipates and the fracture tends to close. Imagine removing the wedge from the log before it splits open all the way. The split log would tend to close up. The same thing happens in a formation when the pressure is released.

Sand is the most common proppant, and workover crews may call fracturing using sand a sandfrac job. Other proppants are aluminum, glass, or plastic beads. Crews test the reservoir to determine the most suitable material for each well. The proppant must be hard enough that it does not flatten out when the hydraulic pressure stops. If it is too hard for the particular rock, on the other hand, the particles can embed in the rock, which also allows the fractures to close (fig. 10.3).

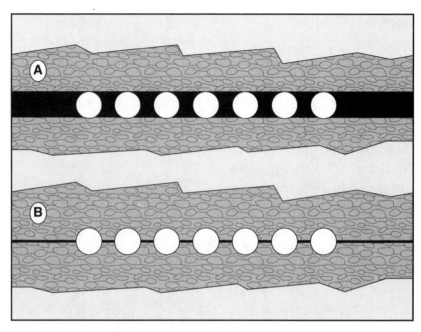

Figure 10.3. Proppants hold the fracture open (A), but if they are harder than the rock, they embed in it and the fracture closes (B).

Fracturing Procedures

Before fracturing, the crew cleans the wellbore, because scale, paraffin, or other materials may plug the perforations. Although the hydraulic pressure might break through the plugged perforations, the fracturing fluid can force these contaminants into the newly created flow channels. Plugged perforations may also force the crew to use a larger pump to create higher pressure or even divert the fractures into another zone.

In addition to cleaning the wellbore, in an old well the crew tests the formation to determine exactly where and why the productivity is low. The permeability may be low either throughout the reservoir or only near the well. Tests may show that low pressure in the reservoir is the problem. In this case, fracturing may not be the right treatment. Tests such as core analyses and drill stem tests can help identify the causes of low productivity.

The crew can set packers to seal off any particular part of the producing zone for fracturing. Crew members may use a single packer or a straddle-packer arrangement, which places packers above and below the area to be fractured (fig. 10.4).

To determine when the formation has fractured, the crew monitors the pressure of the fluid.

Pressure gets higher and higher as the pump forces more fluid into the well. Suddenly, the pressure drops when the rock fractures and the fluid has new places to go.

Then the rig operator often uses sealing balls to fracture a zone that was not affected by the first fracturing procedure (fig. 10.5). Sealing balls work like ball valves. They are made of rubber-coated nylon, and they fit over the perforations to plug them. After the pressure of the fracturing fluid drops, the crew injects the sealing balls into the moving stream of fluid. Pressure from the fluid seats the balls against the perforations that are next to the part of the formation that has already fractured. Pressure again begins to build up, and the fluid fractures through unsealed perforations. The sealing balls fall away from the perforations when the fluid pressure drops. The crew may repeat this two or three times to fracture all desired parts of the formation.

When the job is finished, the crew stops the pumps, bleeds off the pressure, and removes the fracturing equipment. Usually they have to swab the well to restart the flow.

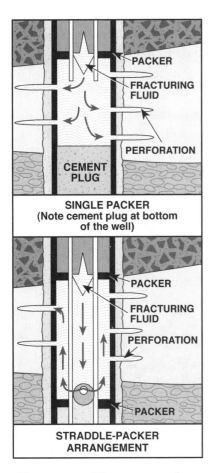

Figure 10.4. The crew can place a packer above the area to be fractured, set packers both above and below the area, or fracture with no packers.

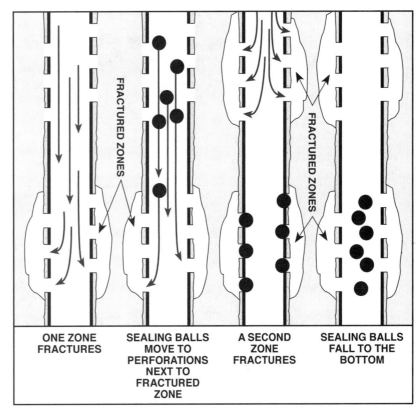

Figure 10.5. Sealing balls seal off a fractured zone so that the fluid will fracture another zone.

Fracturing Equipment

Fracturing does not require a rig, but a special fracturing unit, or frac unit, mounted on a trailer or skid (fig. 10.6). It carries a prime mover, heavy-duty pumps, a transmission, and a control panel. Another option is to use several truck-mounted pumps to provide the pressure needed (see fig. 10.1). For offshore wells, manufacturers put the same equipment on boats or place the skids on barges.

Another piece of equipment necessary for hydraulic fracturing is the blender, which mixes the fracturing fluid with the proppant and additives (fig. 10.7). The blender sits on its own truck. It accurately mixes liquid and dry ingredients using meters and then delivers the fluid to the frac unit.

Figure 10.6. This trailer-mounted fracturing unit carries a control panel, prime mover, transmission, and pump.

Figure 10.7. The blender mixes the fracturing fluid with the propping agent and additives.

ACID STIMULATION

In acid stimulation, or acidizing, an acid reacts chemically with the rock to dissolve it. As in hydraulic fracturing, this enlarges existing flow channels and opens new ones to the wellbore. Well servicing crews stimulate both new and old wells with acid. Reservoir rocks most commonly acidized are limestone (calcium carbonate) and dolomite (a mixture of calcium and magnesium carbonates), or carbonate reservoirs.

Acids that are strong enough to dissolve rock are often strong enough to eat away the metal of the pipes and equipment in the well. Acidizing, therefore, always involves a compromise between acid strength and additives to prevent damage to the equipment.

Types of Acids

Workers on acidizing jobs must be trained to handle the acids they use, many of which have dangerous fumes and can burn the skin. Acidizing contractors choose the type of acid based on the formation and the conditions in the well. Since acidizing uses large volumes of acid, the acid must be fairly inexpensive.

A hydrochloric acid solution is generally the most efficient and economical agent for acidizing carbonate formations. Hydrochloric acid (abbreviated by its chemical formula, HCl) is a strong and hazardous acid, highly corrosive to iron and steel.

If the formation is extremely hot, above 250°F (120°C), or when formation conditions make a weaker, less-corrosive acid more desirable, the acidizing contractor frequently uses a solution of acetic acid and formic acid. Other acids that are sometimes used include sulfamic, nitric, and hydrofluoric acids. The last two are costly and very dangerous. Hydrofluoric acid (also called mud acid) reacts with quartz, which is the main component of sandstones. This acid is poisonous to breathe and is very corrosive to the skin.

The acid is diluted in water. The concentration, or strength, ranges from 3 to 28 percent acid by weight, depending on the type of acid and factors such as reaction time, corrosion hazard, and emulsion-forming properties of the crude oil. The tendency of an acid to form sludges and emulsions with the crude oil in the rocks generally increases with the concentration of the acid solution.

Additives

Whenever an acid reacts with anything in the well, whether rock or metal, it combines with it chemically. A chemical reaction breaks apart the atoms in the compounds put into contact with each other and creates different compounds from the same atoms.

The reaction between acid and rock has two results. First, the acid becomes spent, which means that so much of the acid has reacted with the rock that what is left is too diluted to work. The reaction stops, and fresh acid must be pumped in if the treatment is not complete. Second, the compounds that the reaction forms—reaction products—can interfere with the well's flow. A reaction product may be a precipitate (a solid substance), another liquid, or a gas. Additives counter the effects of the acid and its reaction products.

The chemical reaction is what makes acidizing work, but when acid reacts with the tubing or casing, it is called corrosion. Corrosion will, of course, eat away walls of the tubing or casing, which would be very costly to replace. The most important additive to acid is one to prevent or delay corrosion. Some inhibitors will prevent an acid from corroding steel for ten to twelve hours, even under fairly high bottomhole temperatures (heat speeds up corrosion).

Additives may be surfactants, sequestering agents, or suspending agents. Surfactants prevent acid and oil from forming an emulsion, a mixture like mayonnaise. Sequestering agents prevent minerals that the acid dissolved from reprecipitating, or coming out of the acid solution, on the tubing or casing. These minerals can also plug pores in the rocks, thereby defeating the purpose of the treatment. Suspending agents hold in suspension the precipitates and fine clay particles that sometimes remain after an acidizing treatment. That is, the suspending agent keeps them from settling out of the spent acid until it is circulated out of the hole.

Types of Acidizing Treatments

There are two basic kinds of acid stimulation treatments: acid fracturing, and matrix acidizing. There is one service treatment, spotting.

Acid fracturing, or fracture acidizing, is similar to hydraulic fracturing, except acid is the fluid. Acid fracturing does not require proppants, however, because it not only forces the rock apart, it also eats it away.

It is the more widely used treatment for well stimulation with acid. Since most limestone and dolomite formations have very low permeabilities, injecting acid into these formations, even at a moderate pumping rate, usually results in fracturing.

Matrix acidizing can be subdivided into two types. The first is wellbore cleanup, or wellbore soak. In wellbore soak, the crew fills up the wellbore with acid without any pressure and allows it to react merely by soaking through the perforations. It is a relatively slow process because little of the acid actually comes in contact with the formation. The second matrix acidizing method is a low-pressure treatment that does not fracture the formation, but allows the acid to work through the natural pores. This second process is what people in the oil patch are usually referring to when they speak of matrix acidizing.

The methods for both acid fracturing and matrix acidizing are the same, except for the amount of pressure applied.

Spotting acid means to pump a small amount of acid into a particular spot in a well. Spotting removes deposits on the face (sides) of the producing formation. A rig operator may also spot a well to free stuck drill pipe or to dissolve junk in the hole. This works by corroding the metal.

Acidizing Method

The acidizing crew often pumps a preflush, or spearhead, into the well before the acidizing treatment. A preflush is a liquid that creates a temporary film over some sections of the producing zone that keeps the acid from working in them. For example, an oil preflush allows acid to react with the oil-producing interval of a formation, but blocks acid from the water-producing zones. An HCl preflush before hydrofluoric acid improves this acid's effectiveness in sandstone.

After crew members pump in the acid under low, high, or no pressure, they seal the well to allow the acid to react with the rock. The length of this shut-in time depends on how long it takes for the acid and rock to react, or the reaction time. Reaction time may be zero for HCl in a limestone formation because the acid is spent by the time it is placed. Other acids and formations may require a few hours to acidize. Finally, the crew pumps in a fluid to displace the spent acid and disposes of it.

Sometimes the acidizing crew alternates between pumping acid and pumping a fluid that does not react. This technique allows crew members to select the acidizing zone, for example, by tracking the pumping rate and depth.

Acidizing Equipment

Acidizing units come in many sizes, ranging from small spot treatment trucks to complete acid fracturing units that are similar to hydraulic fracturing units. They all have specially lined tanks and pipes that do not react with the acids. On some units, the mixing system is included right on the same trailer, truck, or skid. Coiled-tubing units for matrix acidizing and spotting are available as well.

II
ADDITIONAL RECOVERY TECHNIQUES

After a well has used up the reservoir's natural drives and all the hydrocarbons possible have been lifted by pumps or gas lift, statistics show that 25 to 95 percent of the oil in the reservoir may remain there. This amount of oil can be worth recovering if prices are high enough. The petroleum industry has developed several techniques to produce at least part of this remaining oil.

One thing to keep in mind about additional recovery techniques is that they are expensive and risky. They require special chemicals, equipment, and personnel. And there are no guarantees that a project will work. Of course, the potential rewards are high if a project does work out, but the risk is also high. In most cases, it takes years before a company actually starts recovering any oil from a project. Recovering oil from reservoirs beyond the initial production remains one of the great challenges facing the oil industry.

WATERFLOODING

When the wells drilled into one reservoir stop flowing, the company representative may hire a workover contractor to pump, or inject, water into some of them (fig. 11.1). The wells into which water is pumped become injection wells. This water kills the wells and then sweeps into the reservoir and moves some of the oil that remains in the rock toward other wells in the same reservoir. These producing wells then pump up the oil and water, often by means of a beam pumping unit. Several injection wells surround each producing well. This procedure is called waterflooding.

Sometimes a crew injects a gas, such as natural gas, nitrogen, or flue gas, in alternating steps with water to improve recovery. In this case it is called gas injection.

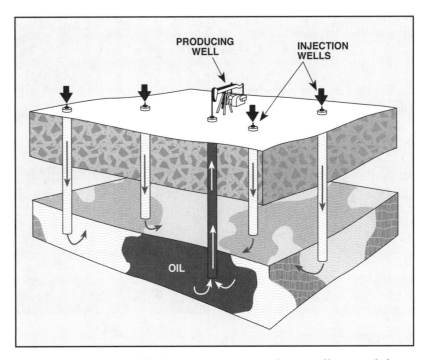

Figure 11.1. In waterflooding, water is injected into wells around the producing well. This is a five-spot pattern—four injection wells and one producer—but many other patterns can be used.

125

Switching wells from producing wells to injection wells is a workover job, but when they need maintenance, a well servicing contractor does the work. Servicing crews frequently work on injection wells in old fields. As they do with producing wells, they maintain the pump and repair or replace tubing if corrosion has caused leaks or if scale has formed.

MISCIBLE DRIVES

While waterflooding recovers additional oil from certain reservoirs, it cannot recover all of it. Part of the reason is that oil and water do not mix—they are not *miscible*. As a result, water will flow past some of the oil and leave it behind. Two processes can improve the amount of oil recovered—chemical flooding and a second type of gas injection.

Chemical Flooding

In chemical flooding, a chemical that causes oil and water to mix can be injected into a reservoir. One chemical that does this is a surfactant. The workover crew injects the surfactant into a well in one of two ways. The first method is to inject a batch, or slug, of water containing the surfactant (fig. 11.2). The second is to inject an alkaline, or caustic, solution. The alkaline solution reacts with the acids normally present in the oil, and the reaction forms a surfactant in the reservoir (fig. 11.3). Whether the surfactant is injected or forms in the reservoir, it washes through it (or at least part of it) and moves additional amounts of oil to the producing well.

Often, the crew mixes a special chemical called a polymer with the water and injects it into the well behind the surfactant. The polymer-water mix helps prevent fingering of the surfactant. Remember that fingering occurs when water moves through sections of the reservoir in "fingers" (see fig 5.2). Fingering leaves portions of the reservoir untouched—portions that contain oil.

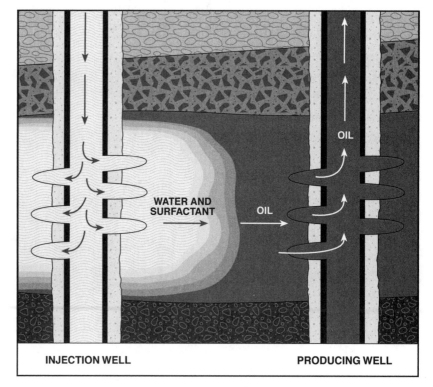

Figure 11.2. In one type of chemical flooding, water containing a surfactant is injected into the reservoir.

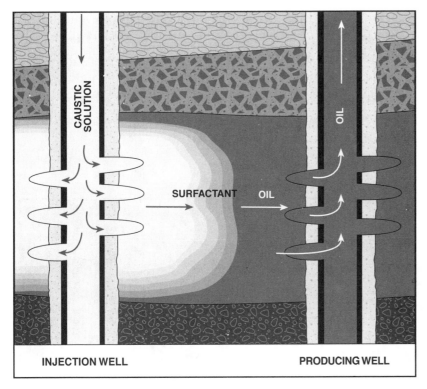

Figure 11.3.   In another type of chemical flooding, a caustic solution is injected and forms a surfactant in the reservoir.

Gas Injection

A gas that is not miscible (mixable) with oil may be injected into a formation, as described under "Waterflooding." A second type of gas injection uses a gas that is miscible with oil to move the oil to the well. Carbon dioxide, propane, or methane are miscible with oil. When a miscible gas is injected, some of its molecules mix with the oil molecules. As injection continues, the gas moves part of the oil to the producing well (fig. 11.4). Usually, the crew injects water behind the gas to minimize the tendency of the gas to rise without mixing with oil in the lower parts of the reservoir.

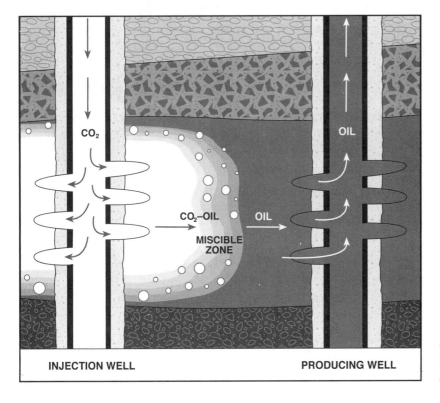

Figure 11.4.   One type of gas injection involves injecting carbon dioxide into the reservoir.

THERMAL PROCESSES

Oil in some reservoirs is so viscous, or thick, that it cannot flow through the reservoir and into a well. Just as tar or other solid materials can be made to flow by heating them, so can some viscous oils. Recovery techniques that use heat are called thermal processes.

Steam Flooding

Steam flooding involves generating steam on the surface and forcing this steam down injection wells and into the reservoir (fig. 11.5). When steam enters the reservoir, it heats up the oil and reduces its viscosity. The

steam flows through the reservoir, cools a little, and condenses (forms hot water). Heat from the steam and hot water vaporizes lighter hydrocarbons, or turns them into gases. These gases move ahead of the steam, cool and condense back into

liquids that dissolve in the oil. In this way, the gases and steam provide additional gas drive. The hot water also moves the thinned oil to production wells, where oil and water are produced.

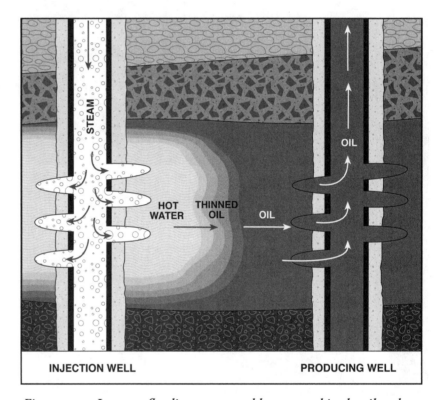

Figure 11.5.   In steam flooding, steam and hot water thin the oil and move it to producing wells. Note that the steam and water override some of the oil, leaving it behind.

Cyclic Steam Injection

Another method is cyclic steam injection, or huff and puff (fig. 11.6). Each huff-and-puff operation involves only one well, but the workover crew may install huff-and-puff equipment on several wells in the oilfield. As in steam flooding, the crew injects hot steam down the well and into the reservoir to heat the oil.

Then steam injection stops, and the rig operator closes in the well and lets the reservoir soak for several days. In the reservoir, the steam condenses and a zone of hot water and less-viscous oil forms. Finally, crew members reopen the well, and the hot water and thinned oil flow out. This process of steam injection, soaking, and production can be repeated until oil recovery stops.

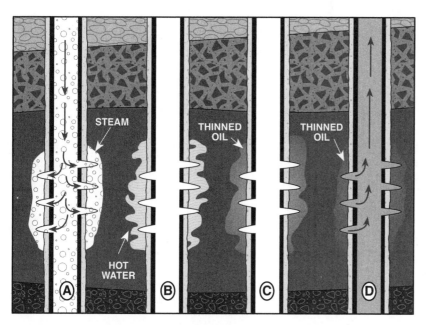

Figure 11.6. In the huff-and-puff method, steam is injected into the reservoir (A). Then the well is closed in and allowed to soak. The steam cools to hot water (B), which thins the oil (C). Finally the thinned oil and hot water are produced (D).

Fire Flooding

Still another way to use heat in a reservoir is fire flooding, or in situ combustion (fig. 11.7). "In situ" means "in place." In fire flooding, the crew ignites a fire in place in the reservoir. To do this, they first inject compressed air down an injection well and into the reservoir, because oil cannot burn without air. A special heater in the well ignites the oil in the reservoir and starts a fire. As the fire burns, it begins moving through the reservoir toward production wells. Heat from the fire thins out the oil around it, causes gas to vaporize from it, and changes water in the reservoir to steam. Steam, hot water, and gas all act to drive oil in front of the fire to production wells.

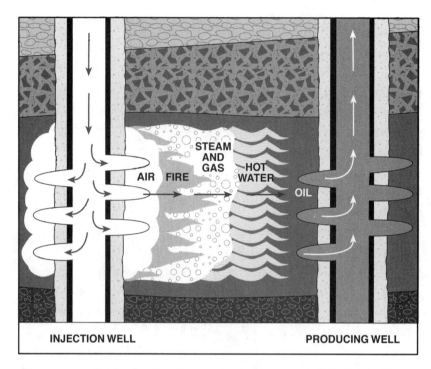

Figure 11.7.   In the fire-flooding method, compressed air is injected into the reservoir, and the oil is ignited. Heat from the fire thins the oil, causes gas to come out, and turns water to steam. Steam, hot water, and gas drive the oil to a producing well.

12
CONCLUSION

The tens of thousands of wells producing all over the world cannot begin to produce or continue to do so efficiently without the efforts of completion, well servicing, and workover personnel. Using sophisticated techniques and equipment, these people start and keep oil and gas flowing, from tiny 10-barrel-a-day "stripper wells" to giant gas wells producing millions of cubic feet (cubic metres) of gas each day.

Whether using a simple truck-mounted swabbing unit or a complicated jackup offshore unit, well service and workover companies the world over keep one of our most vital resources—petroleum—available to us when and where we need it.

GLOSSARY

A

abandon *v*: to cease producing oil and gas from a well when it becomes unprofitable or to cease further work on a newly drilled well when it proves not to contain profitable quantities of oil or gas.

abandoned well *n*: a well not in use because it was a dry hole originally, or because it has ceased to produce. Statutes and regulations in many states require the plugging of abandoned wells to prevent the seepage of oil, gas, or water from one stratum of underlying rock to another.

abnormal pressure *n*: pressure exceeding or falling below the pressure to be expected at a given depth.

abrasion *n*: wearing away by friction.

acetic acid *n*: an organic acid compound sometimes used to acidize oilwells. It is not as corrosive as other acids used in well treatments.

acid fracture *v*: to part or open fractures in productive hard limestone formations by using a combination of oil and acid or water and acid under high pressure. See *fracturing*.

acid gas *n*: a gas that forms an acid when mixed with water. In petroleum production and processing, the most common acid gases are hydrogen sulfide and carbon dioxide.

Both cause corrosion, and hydrogen sulfide is very poisonous.

acidize *v*: to treat oil-bearing limestone or other formations with acid for the purpose of increasing production. Hydrochloric or other acid is injected into the formation under pressure. The acid etches the rock, enlarging the pore spaces and passages through which the reservoir fluids flow. Acid also removes formation damage by dissolving material plugging the rock surrounding the wellbore. The acid is held under pressure for a period of time and then pumped out, after which the well is swabbed and put back into production. Chemical inhibitors combined with the acid prevent corrosion of the pipe.

acid stimulation *n*: a well stimulation method using acid. See *acidize*.

acid wash *n*: an acid treatment in which an acid mixture is circulated through a wellbore to clean it.

acoustic log *n*: a record of the measurement of porosity, done by comparing depth to the time it takes for a sonic impulse to travel through a given length of forma-tion. The rate of travel of the sound wave through a rock depends on the composition of the formation and the fluids it

contains. Because the type of formation can be ascertained by other logs, and because sonic transit time varies with relative amounts of rock and fluid, porosity can usually be determined in this way.

acoustic survey *n*: a well-logging method in which sound impulses are generated and transmitted into the formations opposite the wellbore. The time it takes for the sound impulses to travel through the rock is measured and recorded. Subsequent interpretation of the record (log) permits estimation of the rock's porosity and fluid content.

acoustic well logging *n*: the process of recording the acoustic charateristics of subsurface formations, based on the time required for a sound wave to travel a specific distance through rock. The rate of travel depends on the composition of the formation, its porosity, and its fluid content. Also called sonic logging.

aeration *n*: the injection of air or gas into a liquid. In the oil industry a common form of aeration is the injection of natural gas into reservoir liquids standing in a well. Aeration with natural gas reduces the density of the liquids and allows declining reservoir pressure to lift the liquids. See *gas lift*.

AESC *abbr*: Association of Energy Service Companies.

alkaline (caustic) flooding *n*: a method of additional recovery in which alkaline chemicals such as sodium hydroxide are injected during a waterflood or combined with polymer flooding. The chemicals react with the natural acid present in certain crude oils to form surfactants within the reservoir. The surfactants enable the water to move additional quantities of oil from the depleted reservoir. Compare *chemical flooding, polymer flooding, waterflooding.*

alloy *n*: a substance with metallic properties that comprises two or more elements in solid solution. See *ferrous alloy, nonferrous alloy.*

American Petroleum Institute (API) *n*: oil trade organization (founded in 1920) that is the leading standardizing organization for oilfield drilling and producing equipment. It maintains departments of transportation, refining, and marketing in Washington, DC. Its official publications are *Petroleum Today, Washington Report,* and hundreds of standards, recommended practices, and bulletins. Address: 1220 L St., NW; Washington, DC 20005; (202) 682-8000.

annular blowout preventer *n*: a large valve, usually installed above the ram preventers, that forms a seal in the annular space between the pipe and the wellbore or, if no pipe is present, in the wellbore itself. Compare *ram blowout preventer.*

annular pressure *n*: fluid pressure in an annular space, as around tubing within casing.

annular production *n*: production of formation fluids through the production casing annulus.

annular space *n*: see *annulus.*

annular velocity *n*: the rate at which mud is traveling in the annular space of a drilling well.

annulus *n*: the space between two concentric circles. In the petroleum industry, it is usually the space surrounding a pipe in the wellbore.

API *abbr*: American Petroleum Institute.

API-certified *adj*: said of a tool that meets the American Petroleum Institute's minimum standards.

artificial lift *n*: any method used to raise oil to the surface through a well after reservoir pressure has declined to the point at which the well no longer produces by means of natural energy. Sucker rod pumps, gas lift, hydraulic pumps, and submersible electric pumps are the most common means of artificial lift.

Association of Energy Service Companies (AESC) *n*: organization that sets some of the standards, principles, and policies of oilwell servicing contractors. Its official publication is *Well Servicing.* Address: 6060 N. Central Expressway, Suite 428; Dallas, TX 75206; (214) 692-0771.

B

back-in unit *n*: a portable servicing or workover rig that is self-propelled, using the hoisting engines for motive power. Because the driver's cab is mounted on the end opposite the mast support, the unit must be backed up to the wellhead. Compare *carrier rig, drive-in unit.*

back off *v*: to unscrew one threaded piece (such as a section of pipe) from another.

bailer *n*: a long, cylindrical container fitted with a valve at its lower end, used to remove water, sand, mud, drilling cuttings, or oil from a well in cable-tool drilling.

ball-and-seat valve *n*: a device used to restrict fluid flow to one direction. It consists of a polished sphere, or ball, usually of metal, and an annular piece, the seat, ground and polished to form a seal with the surface of the ball. Gravitational force or the force of a spring holds the ball against the seat. Flow in the direction of the force is prevented, while flow in the opposite direction overcomes the force and unseats the ball.

ball sealers *n pl*: balls made of nylon, hard rubber, or both and used to shut off perforations through which excessive fluid is being lost.

barefoot completion *n*: see *openhole completion.*

barite *n*: barium sulfate, $BaSO_4$; a mineral frequently used to increase the weight or density of drilling mud. Its relative density is 4.2 (i.e., it is 4.2 times denser than water). See *barium sulfate.*

barium sulfate *n*: a chemical compound of barium, sulfur, and oxygen ($BaSO_4$), which may form a tenacious scale that is very difficult to remove. Also called barite.

basket *n*: a device placed in the drill or work string that catches debris when a drillable object is being milled or drilled downhole.

beam pumping unit *n*: a machine designed specifically for sucker rod pumping. An engine or motor (prime mover) is mounted on the unit to power a rotating crank. The crank moves a horizontal member (walking beam) up and down to produce reciprocating motion. This reciprocating motion operates the pump. Compare *pump jack*.

bent housing *n*: a special housing for the positive-displacement downhole mud motor, which is manufactured with a bend of 1° to 3° to facilitate directional drilling.

bent sub *n*: a short cylindrical device installed in the drill stem between the bottommost drill collar and a downhole motor. Its purpose is to deflect the downhole motor off vertical to drill a directional hole.

bit *n*: the cutting or boring element used in drilling oil and gas wells. The bit consists of a cutting element that gouges or scrapes the formation to remove it and a circulating element that permits the passage of drilling fluid and uses the hydraulic force of the fluid stream to improve drilling rates.

bleed *v*: to drain off liquid or gas, generally slowly, through a valve called a bleeder. To bleed down, or bleed off, means to release pressure slowly from a well or from pressurized equipment.

blowout preventer *n*: one of several valves installed at the wellhead to prevent the escape of pressure either in the annular space between the casing and the drill pipe or in open hole during drilling, completion, and workover operations. Blowout preventers on land rigs are located beneath the rig at the land's surface; on jackup or platform rigs, at the water's surface; and on floating offshore rigs, on the seafloor. See *annular blowout preventer, ram blowout preventer*.

boot sub *n*: a device made up in the drill stem above the mill to collect bits of junk ground away during a milling operation. During milling, drilling mud under high pressure forces bits of junk up the narrow space between the boot sub and hole wall. When the junk reaches the wider annulus above the boot sub and pressure drops slightly, the junk falls into the boot sub. A boot sub also can be run above the bit during routine drilling to collect small pieces of junk that may damage the bit or interfere with its operation. Also called a junk sub or junk boot.

BOP *abbr*: blowout preventer.

bottomhole plug *n*: a bridge plug or cement plug placed near the bottom of the hole to shut off a depleted, water-producing, or unproductive zone.

bottomhole pressure *n*: 1. the pressure at the bottom of a borehole. It is caused by the hydrostatic pressure of the wellbore fluid and, sometimes, by any back-pressure held at the surface, as when the well is shut in with blowout preventers. When mud is being circulated, bottomhole pressure is the hydrostatic pressure plus the remaining circulating pressure required to move the mud up the annulus. 2. the pressure in a well at a point opposite the producing formation, as recorded by a bottomhole pressure bomb.

bottomhole pressure test *n*: a test that measures the reservoir pressure of the well, obtained at a specific depth or at the midpoint of the producing zone. A flowing bottomhole pressure test measures pressure while the well continues to flow; a shut-in bottomhole pressure test measures pressure while the well has been shut in for a specified period of time.

bottomhole pump *n*: any of the rod pumps, high-pressure liquid pumps, or centrifugal pumps located at or near the bottom of the well and used to lift the well fluids. See *centrifugal pump, hydraulic pumping, submersible pump, sucker rod pumping*.

bradenhead *n*: (obsolete) casinghead. Glen T. Braden invented a casinghead in the 1920s that became so popular that all casingheads were called bradenheads.

bradenhead squeeze *n*: a process used to repair a hole in the casing by pumping cement down tubing or drill pipe. Although the term "bradenhead squeezing" is still used, the term "bradenhead" is obsolete. See *casinghead, squeeze*.

break out *v*: 1. to unscrew one section of pipe from another section, especially drill pipe while it is being withdrawn from the wellbore. 2. to separate, as gas from a liquid or water from an emulsion.

bridge plug *n*: a downhole tool, composed primarily of slips, a plug mandrel, and a rubber sealing element, that is run and set in casing to isolate a lower zone while an upper section is being tested or cemented.

brine *n*: water that has a large quantity of salt, especially sodium chloride, dissolved in it; salt water.

bullet perforator *n*: a tubular device that, when lowered to a selected depth within a well, fires bullets through the casing to provide holes through which the formation fluids may enter the wellbore.

bull shaft *n*: see *crankshaft*.

bumper jar *n*: a device made up in the drill string that, when actuated, delivers a heavy downward blow to the string. If downward blows can free a fish, a bumper jar can be very effective.

bumper sub *n*: a percussion tool run on a fishing string to jar downward or upward on a stuck fish to knock it free. The bumper sub body moves up and down on a mandrel.

burn shoe *n*: see *rotary shoe*.

C

caliper log *n*: a record showing variations in wellbore diameter by depth, indicating undue enlargement due to caving in, washout, or other causes. The caliper log also reveals corrosion, scaling, or pitting inside tubular goods.

carbonate rock *n*: a sedimentary rock composed primarily of calcium carbonate (calcite) or calcium magnesium carbonate (dolomite).

carrier rig *n*: a large, self-propelled workover rig that is driven directly to the well site. Power from a carrier rig's hoist engine or engines also propels the rig on the road. While a carrier rig is primarily intended to perform workovers, it can also be used to drill relatively shallow wells. A carrier rig may be a back-in type or a drive-in type. Compare *back-in unit, drive-in unit*.

carrier unit *n*: see *carrier rig*.

cased-hole fishing *n*: the procedure of recovering lost or stuck equipment in a wellbore in which casing has been run.

casing *n*: steel pipe placed in an oil or gas well to prevent the wall of the hole from caving in, to prevent movement of fluids from one formation to another, and to improve the efficiency of extracting petroleum if the well is productive. A joint of casing may be 16 to 48 feet (4.8 to 14.6 metres) long and from 4.5 to 20 inches (11.4 to 50.8 centimetres) in diameter. Casing is made of many types of steel alloy, which vary in strength, corrosion resistance, and so on.

casing collar *n*: a coupling between two joints.

casing coupling *n*: a tubular section of pipe that is threaded inside and used to connect two joints of casing.

casing cutter *n*: a heavy cylindrical body, fitted with a set of knives, used to free a section of casing in a well. The cutter is run downhole on a string of tubing or drill pipe, and the knives are rotated against the inner walls of the casing to free the section that is stuck.

casing gun *n*: a perforating gun run into the casing string.

casing hanger *n*: a circular device with a frictional gripping arrangement of slips and packing rings used to suspend casing from a casinghead in a well.

casinghead *n*: a heavy, flanged steel fitting connected to the first string of casing. It provides a housing for slips and packing assemblies, allows suspension of intermediate and production strings of casing, and supplies the means for the annulus to be sealed off. Also called spool.

casing overshot *n*: a special tool with a rubber packer or lead seal that is used to repair casing.

casing roller *n*: a tool composed of a mandrel on which are mounted several heavy-duty rollers with eccentric roll surfaces. It is used to restore buckled, collapsed, or dented casing in a well to normal diameter and roundness.

casing shoe *n*: see *guide shoe*.

casing-tubing annulus *n*: in a wellbore, the space between the inside of the casing and the outside of the tubing.

cement *n*: a powder consisting of alumina, silica, lime, and other substances that hardens when mixed with water. Extensively used in the oil industry to bond casing to the walls of the wellbore.

cement bond *n*: the adherence of casing to cement and cement to formation.

cement bond survey *n*: an acoustic logging method based on the fact that sound travels at different speeds through materials of different densities. This fact can be used to determine whether the cement has bonded properly to the casing. Compare *acoustic survey, acoustic well logging*.

cementing *n*: the application of a liquid slurry of cement and water to various points inside or outside the casing. See *plug-back cementing, squeeze cementing*.

cement plug *n*: a portion of cement placed at some point in the wellbore to seal it. See *cementing*.

cement retainer *n*: a tool set temporarily in the casing or well to prevent the passage of cement, thereby forcing it to follow another designated path. It is used in squeeze cementing and other remedial cementing jobs.

centralizer *n*: a device that centers casing, liner, or a tool in the well.

centrifugal pump *n*: a pump with an impeller or rotor, an impeller shaft, and a casing, which discharges fluid by centrifugal force. An electric submersible pump is a centrifugal pump.

channeling *n*: when casing is being cemented in a borehole, the cement slurry can fail to rise uniformly between the casing and the borehole wall, leaving spaces, or channels, devoid of cement. Ideally, the cement should completely and uniformly surround the casing and form a strong bond to the borehole wall.

chemical consolidation *n*: the procedure by which a quantity of resinous material is squeezed into a sandy formation to consolidate the sand and to prevent its flowing into the well. The resinous material hardens and creates a porous mass that permits oil to flow into the well but holds back the sand at the same time. See *sand consolidation*.

chemical cutoff *n*: a method of severing steel pipe in a well by applying high-pressure jets of a very corrosive substance against the wall of the pipe.

chemical cutter *n*: a fishing tool that uses high-pressure jets of chemicals to sever casing, tubing, or drill pipe stuck in the hole.

chemical flooding *n*: a method of improved oil recovery in which chemicals dissolved in water are pumped into a reservoir through injection wells to mobilize oil left behind after primary or secondary recovery and to move it toward production wells. See *miscible drive, polymer flooding*. Compare *alkaline (caustic) flooding, gas injection, polymer flooding, waterflooding*.

Christmas tree *n*: the control valves, pressure gauges, and chokes assembled at the top of a well to control the flow of oil and gas after the well has been drilled and completed. It is used when reservoir pressure is sufficient to cause reservoir fluids to flow to the surface.

circulation *n*: the process of pumping a fluid down the well and back up to the surface in a drilling or workover operation. See *normal circulation, reverse circulation*.

circulation valve *n*: an accessory employed above a packer to permit annulus-to-tubing circulation or vice versa.

clean out *v*: to remove sand, scale, and other deposits from the producing section of the well to restore or increase production.

cleanout tools *n pl*: the tools or instruments, such as bailers and swabs, used to clean out an oilwell.

coiled tubing *n*: a continuous string of flexible steel tubing, often several hundred or thousands of feet (metres) long, that is collected onto a reel, much as fishing line is wound on a reel. The reel is an integral part of a coiled tubing unit, which consists of several devices that ensure that the tubing can be safely and efficiently inserted into the well from the surface. Because the tubing can be lowered into the well without having to make up joints of tubing, running coiled tubing into the well is faster and less expensive than running conventional tubing.

coiled-tubing unit *n*: the equipment for transporting and using coiled tubing, including a reel for the coiled tubing, an injector head to push the tubing down the well, a wellhead blowout preventer stack, a power source (usually a diesel engine and hydraulic pumps), and a control console. A unique feature of the unit is that it allows continuous circulation while it is being lowered into the hole. A coiled tubing unit is usually mounted on a trailer or skid.

coiled-tubing workover *n*: a workover performed with coiled tubing.

collar locator *n*: a logging device used to determine accurately the depth of a well; the log measures and records the depth of each casing collar, or coupling, in a well.

collar locator log *n*: see *collar locator*.

combination drive *n*: a combination of two or more natural energies that work together in a reservoir to force fluids into a wellbore. Possible combinations include gas-cap and water drive, dissolved-gas and water drive, and gas-cap drive and gravity drainage.

commercial amount *n*: an amount of oil and gas production large enough to enable the operator to realize a profit, however small. To keep the lease in force, production must be in quantities sufficient to yield a return in excess of operating costs, even though drilling and equipment costs may never be recovered.

company man *n*: see *company representative*.

company representative *n*: an employee of an oil company who supervises the operations at a drilling site or well site and coordinates the hiring of logging, testing, service, and workover companies. Also called company man.

completion fluid *n*: low-solids fluid or drilling mud used when a well is being completed. It is selected not only for its ability to control formation pressure, but also for the properties that minimize formation damage.

conductivity *n*: 1. the ability to transmit or convey (as heat or electricity). 2. an electrical logging measurement obtained from an induction survey. See *induction log*.

conductor casing *n*: generally, the first string of casing in a well. Its purpose is to prevent the soft formations near the surface from caving in and to conduct drilling mud from the bottom of the hole to the surface when drilling starts. Also called conductor pipe, drive pipe.

conductor line *n*: a small-diameter conductive line used in electric wireline operations, such as electric well logging and perforating, in which the transmission of electrical current is required. Compare *wireline*.

conductor pipe *n*: see *conductor casing*.

consultant *n*: a person who contracts with an oil company to supervise the operations at a drilling site or well site and coordinate the hiring of logging, testing, service, and workover companies.

continuous flowmeter log *n*: see *spinner survey*.

continuous steam injection *n*: see *steam flooding*.

conventional pump *n*: see *fixed pump*.

core *n*: a cylindrical sample taken from a formation for geological analysis. *v*: to obtain a solid, cylindrical formation sample for analysis.

core analysis *n*: laboratory analysis of a core sample to determine porosity, permeability, lithology, fluid content, angle of dip, geological age, and probable productivity of the formation.

core sample *n*: a small portion of a formation obtained by using a coring bit in an existing wellbore. See *coring bit*.

coring *n*: the process of cutting a vertical, cylindrical sample of the formations encountered as an oilwell is drilled.

coring bit *n*: a bit that does not drill out the center portion of the hole, but allows this center portion (the core) to pass through the round opening in the center of the bit and into the core barrel.

corrosion *n*: any of a variety of complex chemical or electrochemical processes (for example, rust) by which metal is destroyed through reaction with its environment.

corrosion inhibitor *n*: a chemical substance that minimizes or prevents corrosion in metal equipment.

counterbalance weight *n*: a weight applied to compensate for existing weight or force. On pumping units in oil production, counterweights are used to offset the weight of the column of sucker rods and fluid on the upstroke of the pump, and the weight of the rods on the downstroke.

coupling *n*: in piping, a metal collar with internal threads used to join two sections of threaded pipe.

crank *n*: an arm keyed at right angles to a shaft and used for changing radius of rotation or changing reciprocating motion to circular motion or circular motion to reciprocating motion. On a beam pumping unit, the crank is connected by the pitman to the walking beam, thereby changing circular motion to reciprocating motion.

crank arm *n*: see *crank*.

crankshaft *n*: a rotating shaft to which connecting rods are attached. It changes up and down (reciprocating) motion to circular (rotary) motion.

crew chief *n*: see *unit operator*.

crooked hole *n*: a wellbore that has been unintentionally drilled in a direction other than vertical. It usually occurs where there is a section of alternating hard and soft strata steeply inclined from the horizontal.

crown block *n*: an assembly of sheaves mounted on beams at the top of the derrick or mast and over which the drilling line is reeved.

cuttings *n pl*: the fragments of rock dislodged by the bit and brought to the surface in the drilling mud. Washed and dried cuttings samples are analyzed by geologists to obtain information about the formations drilled.

cuttings-sample log *n*: a record of hydrocarbon content in cuttings gathered at the shale shaker; usually recorded on the mud log.

cyclic steam injection *n*: a method of recovering reservoir oil that is too viscous to flow. Steam is injected into a well, the well is closed in and allowed to soak for several days, which thins the oil so that it can be produced. Also called huff and puff. Compare *steam flooding, thermal recovery*.

D

deflection *n*: a change in the angle of a wellbore. In directional drilling, it is measured in degrees from the vertical.

deflection tool *n*: a device made up in the drill string that causes the bit to drill at an angle to the existing hole. It is often called a kickoff tool, because it is used at the kickoff point to start building angle.

density log *n*: a special radioactivity log for open-hole surveying that responds to variations in the specific gravity of formations. The density log is an excellent porosity-measure device, especially for shaley sands.

depletion drive *n*: see *gas drive*.

derrick *n*: a large load-bearing structure, usually of bolted construction. In drilling, the standard derrick has four legs standing at the corners of the substructure and reaching to the crown block. The substructure is an assembly of heavy beams used to elevate the derrick and provide space to install blowout preventers, casingheads, and so forth. Because the standard derrick must be assembled piece by piece, it has largely been replaced by the mast, which can be lowered and raised without disassembly.

derrickhand *n*: the crew member who handles the upper part of the tubing or work string as it is being hoisted out of or lowered into the hole. On a drilling rig, he or she is also responsible for the circulating machinery and the condition of the drilling or workover fluid.

die collar *n*: a steel collar or coupling, threaded internally, that can be used to retrieve a tubular fish. If the fish is stuck so that it cannot rotate, rotating the die collar cuts threads on the outside of the fish, providing a firm attachment to retrieve the fish. It is not often used because it is difficult to release it from the fish should it become necessary. Compare *taper tap*.

dipmeter log *n*: see *dipmeter survey*.

dipmeter survey *n*: an oilwell-surveying method that determines the direction and angle of formation dip in relation to the borehole. It records data that permit computation of both the amount and direction of formation dip relative to the axis of the hole and thus provides information about the geologic structure of the formation. Also called dipmeter log or dip log.

directional drilling *n*: intentional deviation of a wellbore from the vertical. Although wellbores are normally drilled vertically, it is sometimes necessary or advantageous to drill at an angle from the vertical. Controlled directional drilling makes it possible to reach subsurface areas laterally remote from the point where the bit enters the earth. It often involves the use of deflection tools.

directional hole *n*: a wellbore intentionally drilled at an angle from the vertical. See *directional drilling*.

displacement *n*: replacement of one fluid by another in the pore space of a reservoir. For example, oil may be displaced by water.

dissolved gas *n*: natural gas that is in solution with crude oil in the reservoir.

dissolved-gas drive *n*: a source of natural reservoir energy in which the dissolved gas coming out of the oil expands to force the oil into the wellbore. Also called solution-gas drive. See *reservoir drive mechanism*.

dogleg *n*: 1. an abrupt change in direction in the wellbore, frequently resulting in the formation of a keyseat. 2. a sharp bend permanently put in an object such as a pipe.

downhole motor *n*: a drilling tool made up in the drill string directly above the bit. It causes the bit to turn while the drill string remains fixed. It is used most often as a deflection tool in directional drilling, where it is made up between the bit and a bent sub (or sometimes, the housing of the motor itself is bent). Also called mud motor.

drainage *n*: the migration of oil or gas in a reservoir toward a wellbore due to pressure reduction caused by the well's penetration of the reservoir. A drainage point is a wellbore (or in some cases, several wellbores) that drains the reservoir.

drawworks *n*: the hoisting mechanism on a drilling rig. It is essentially a large winch that spools off or takes in the drilling line and thus raises or lowers the drill stem.

drillable *adj*: pertaining to packers and other tools left in the wellbore to be broken up later by the drill bit. Drillable equipment is made of cast iron, aluminum, plastic, or other soft, brittle material.

drillable packer *n*: a permanent packer that can only be removed by drilling it out.

drill collar *n*: a heavy, thick-walled tube, usually steel, placed between the drill pipe and the bit in the drill stem. Several drill collars are used to provide weight on the bit and to provide a pendulum effect to the drill stem.

driller *n*: the employee directly in charge of a drilling or workover rig and crew. The driller's main duty is operation of the drilling and hoisting equipment, but this crew member is also responsible for downhole condition of the well, operation of downhole tools, and pipe measurements.

driller's log *n*: a record that describes each formation encountered and lists the drilling time relative to depth, usually in 5- to 10-foot (1.5- to 3-metre) intervals.

drilling contractor *n*: an individual or group that owns a drilling rig or rigs and contracts services for drilling wells.

drilling crew *n*: a driller, a derrickhand, and two or more helpers who operate a drilling or workover rig for one tour each day.

drilling fluid *n*: circulating fluid, one function of which is to lift cuttings out of the wellbore and to the surface. Other functions are to cool the bit and to counteract downhole formation pressure. Although a mixture of barite, clay, water, and chemical additives is the most common drilling fluid, wells can also be drilled by using air, gas, water, or oil-base mud as the drilling mud.

drilling line *n*: a wire rope used to support the drilling tools.

drilling mud *n*: see *drilling fluid*.

drill out *v*: 1. to remove with the bit the residual cement that normally remains in the lower section of casing and the wellbore after the casing has been cemented. 2. to remove the settlings and cavings that are plugged inside a hollow fish (such as drill pipe) during a fishing operation.

drill pipe *n*: seamless steel or aluminum pipe made up in the drill stem between the kelly or top drive on the surface and the drill collars on the bottom. During drilling, it is usually rotated while drilling fluid is circulated through it.

drill stem *n*: all members in the assembly used for rotary drilling from the swivel to the bit, including the kelly, drill pipe and tool joints, drill collars, stabilizers, and various specialty items. Compare *drill string*.

drill stem test (DST) *n*: the conventional method of formation testing. The basic drill stem test tool consists of a packer or packers, valves or ports that may be opened and closed from the surface, and two or more pressure-recording devices. The packer or packers isolate the testing zone from the drilling fluid column. The valves or ports are then opened to allow for formation flow while the recorders chart static pressures. A sampling chamber traps clean formation fluids at the end of the test. Analysis of the pressure charts is an important part of formation testing.

drill string *n*: the column, or string, of drill pipe with attached tool joints that transmits fluid and rotational power from the kelly to the drill collars and bit. Often, especially in the oil patch, the term is loosely applied to both drill pipe and drill collars. Compare *drill stem*.

drive *n*: 1. the means by which a machine is given motion or power, or by which power is transferred from one part of a machine to another. 2. the energy of expanding gas, inflowing water, or other natural or artificial mechanisms that forces crude oil out of the reservoir formation and into the wellbore. *v*: to give motion or power.

drive-in unit *n*: a type of portable service or workover rig that is self-propelled, using power from the hoisting engines. The driver's cab and steering wheel are mounted on the same end as the mast support; thus the unit can be driven straight ahead to reach the wellhead. Compare *back-in unit, carrier rig*.

drive pipe *n*: see *conductor casing*.

DST *abbr*: drill stem test.

DST tool *n*: drill stem test tool; used for formation evaluation.

dual completion *n*: a single well that produces from two separate formations at the same time. Production from each zone is segregated by running two tubing strings with packers inside the single string of production casing, or by running one tubing string with a packer through one zone while the other is produced through the annulus.

dump bailer *n*: a bailing device with a release valve, usually of the disk or flapper type, used to place, or spot, material (such as cement slurry) at the bottom of the well.

E

electric log *n*: see *electric well log*.

electric submersible pumping *n*: a form of artificial lift that utilizes an electric submersible multistage centrifugal pump. Electric power is conducted to the pump by a cable attached to the tubing.

electric survey *n*: see *electric well log*.

electric well log *n*: a record of certain electrical characteristics (such as resistivity and conductivity) of formations traversed by the borehole. It is made to identify the formations, determine the nature and amount of fluids they contain, and estimate their depth. Also called an electric log or electric survey.

engine *n*: a machine for converting the heat content of fuel into rotary motion that can be used to power other machines. Compare *motor*.

erosion *n*: the process by which material (such as rock or soil) is worn away or removed (as by wind or water).

expendable gun *n*: a perforating gun that consists of a metal strip on which are mounted shaped charges in special capsules. After firing, nothing remains of the gun but debris. See *perforate*.

external cutter *n*: a fishing tool containing metal-cutting knives that is lowered into the hole and over the outside of a length of pipe to cut it. The severed part of the pipe can then be brought to the surface. Also called an outside cutter. Compare *internal cutter*.

F

ferrous alloy *n*: a metal alloy in which iron is a major component.

fingering *n*: 1. a phenomenon that often occurs in an injection project in which the fluid being injected does not contact the entire reservoir but bypasses sections of the reservoir fluids in a fingerlike manner. Fingering is not desirable, because portions of the reservoir are not contacted by the injection fluid. 2. the same phenomenon in which water bypasses oil in the reservoir on its way to the well.

fire flooding *n*: a thermal recovery method in which the oil in the reservoir is ignited, the heat vaporizes lighter hydrocarbons and water and pushes the warmed oil toward a producing well. Also called in situ combustion. See *thermal recovery*.

fish *n*: an object that is left in the wellbore during drilling or workover operations and that must be recovered before work can proceed. *v*: 1. to recover from a well any equipment left there during drilling operations, such as a lost bit or drill collar or part of the drill string. 2. to remove from an older well certain pieces of equipment (such as packers, liners, or screen liner) to allow reconditioning of the well.

fishing assembly *n*: see *fishing string*.

fishing magnet *n*: a powerful permanent magnet designed to recover metallic objects lost in a well.

fishing string *n*: an assembly of tools made up on drill pipe that is lowered into the hole to retrieve lost or stuck equipment. Also called a fishing assembly.

fishing tool *n*: a tool designed to recover equipment lost in a well.

fishing-tool operator *n*: the person (usually a service company employee) in charge of directing fishing operations.

fixed pump *n*: a type of downhole hydraulic pump that is attached to the end of tubing; the tubing must be pulled to service the pump. See *hydraulic pumping*. Compare *free pump*.

flood *v*: 1. to drive oil from a reservoir into a well by injecting water under pressure into the reservoir formation. See *waterflooding*. 2. to drown out a well with water.

floorhand *n*: see *rotary helper*.

floorman *n*: see *rotary helper*.

flowing well *n*: a well that produces oil or gas by its own reservoir pressure rather than by use of artificial means (such as pumps).

flow line *n*: the surface pipe through which oil travels from a well to processing equipment or to storage.

flow rate *n*: the speed, or velocity, of fluid flow through a pipe or vessel.

fluid injection *n*: injection of gases or liquids into a reservoir to force oil toward and into producing wells.

fluid loss *n*: the unwanted migration of the liquid part of the drilling mud or cement slurry into a formation, often minimized or prevented by the blending of additives with the mud or cement.

formation damage *n*: the reduction of permeability in a reservoir rock caused by the invasion of drilling fluid and treating fluids to the section adjacent to the wellbore. Also called skin damage.

formation fluid *n*: fluid (such as gas, oil, or water) that exists in a subsurface rock formation.

formation gas *n*: gas initially produced from an underground reservoir.

formation pressure *n*: the force exerted by fluids in a formation, recorded in the hole at the level of the formation with the well shut in. Also called reservoir pressure or shut-in bottomhole pressure.

formation strength *n*: the ability of a formation to resist fracture from pressures created by fluids in a borehole.

formation tester *n*: see *wireline formation tester*.

formation testing *n*: the gathering of pressure data and fluid samples from a formation to determine its production potential before choosing a completion method. Formation testing tools include formation testers and drill stem test tools.

formation water *n*: 1. the water originally in place in a formation. 2. any water that resides in the pore spaces of a formation.

frac *abbr*: fractured or fracturing.

frac fluid *n*: see *fracturing fluid*.

frac job *n*: see *fracturing*.

fracture *n*: a crack or crevice in a formation, either natural or induced. See *acid fracture, hydraulic fracturing*.

fracture acidizing *n*: a procedure by which acid is forced into a formation under pressure high enough to cause the formation to crack. The acid acts on certain kinds of rocks, usually carbonates, to increase the permeability of the formation. Also called *acid fracture*. Compare *matrix acidizing*.

fracture pressure *n*: the pressure at which a formation will break down, or fracture.

fracturing *n*: a method of stimulating production by opening new flow channels in the rock surrounding a production well. Often called a frac job. See *acid fracture, hydraulic fracturing*.

fracturing fluid *n*: a fluid, such as water, oil, or acid, used in hydraulic fracturing. The fluid carries propping agents that hold open the formation cracks after hydraulic pressure dissipates. See *acid fracture, hydraulic fracturing, propping agents*.

free-point indicator *n*: a device run on wireline into the wellbore and inside the fishing string and fish to locate the area where a fish is stuck. When the drill string is pulled and turned, the electromagnetic fields of free pipe and stuck pipe differ. The free-point indicator is able to distinguish these differences, which are registered on a metering device at the surface.

free pump *n*: a type of downhole hydraulic pump that moves in and out of the well by means of circulating fluids. See *hydraulic pump*. Compare *fixed pump*.

freeze point *n*: the depth in the hole at which the tubing, casing, or drill pipe is stuck. See *free-point indicator*.

friction *n*: resistance to movement created when two surfaces are in contact. When friction is present, movement between the surfaces produces heat.

frictional resistance *n*: the opposition to flow created by a fluid when it flows through a line or other con-tainer. Frictional resistance occurs within the fluid itself and it is created by the walls of the pipe or container as the fluid flows past them.

G

galvanic corrosion *n*: a type of corrosion that occurs when a small electric current flows from one piece of metal equipment to another. It is particularly prevalent when two dissimilar metals are present in an environment in which electricity can flow (as two dissimilar joints of tubing in an oil or gas well).

gamma ray log *n*: a type of radioactivity well log that records natural radioactivity around the wellbore. Shales generally produce higher levels of gamma radiation and can be detected and studied with the gamma ray tool. In holes where salty drilling fluids are used, electric logging tools are less effective than gamma ray tools. See *radioactivity well logging*.

gas anchor *n*: a tubular, perforated device attached to the bottom of a sucker-rod pump that helps prevent gas lock. The device works on the principle that gas, being lighter than oil, rises. As well fluids enter the anchor, the gas breaks out of the fluid and exits from the anchor through perforations near the top. The remaining fluids enter the pump through a mosquito bill (a tube within the anchor), which has an opening near the bottom. In this way, all or most of the gas escapes before the fluids enter the pump.

gas cap *n*: a free-gas phase overlying an oil zone and occurring within the same producing formation as the oil. See *reservoir*.

gas-cap drive *n*: drive energy supplied naturally (as a reservoir is produced) by the expansion of the gas cap. In such a drive, the gas cap expands to force oil into the well and to the surface. See *reservoir drive mechanism*.

gas drive *n*: the use of the energy that arises from the expansion of compressed gas in a reservoir to move crude oil to a wellbore. Also called depletion drive. See *dissolved-gas drive, gas-cap drive, reservoir drive mechanism*.

gas injection *n*: the injection of gas into a reservoir to maintain formation pressure by gas drive and to reduce the rate of decline of the original reservoir drive. One type of gas injection uses gas that does not mix (i.e., that is not miscible) with the oil. Another type uses gas that does mix (i.e., that is miscible) with the oil. The gas may be naturally miscible or become miscible under high pressure. Frequently, water is also injected in alternating steps with the gas.

gas injection well *n*: a well into which gas is injected for the purpose of maintaining or supplementing pressure in an oil reservoir.

gas lift *n*: the process of raising or lifting fluid from a well by injecting gas down the well through tubing or through the tubing-casing annulus. Gas may be injected continuously or intermittently, depending on the producing characteristics of the well and the arrangement of the gas lift equipment.

gas-lift mandrel *n*: a device installed in the tubing string of a gas-lift well onto which or into which a gas-lift valve is fitted.

gas-lift valve *n*: a device installed on a gas-lift mandrel, which in turn is put on the tubing string of a gas-lift well. Tubing and casing pressures cause the valve to open and close, thus allowing gas to be injected into the fluid in the tubing to cause the fluid to rise to the surface.

gas-lift well *n*: a well in which reservoir fluids are artificially lifted by the injection of gas.

gas lock *n*: a condition sometimes encountered in a pumping well when dissolved gas, released from solution during the upstroke of the plunger, appears as free gas between the valves. If the gas pressure is sufficient, the standing valve is locked shut, and no fluid enters the tubing.

gas well *n*: a well that primarily produces gas. Legal definitions vary among the states.

gear reducer *n*: see *speed reducer*.

gel *n*: a jellylike semisolid. When agitated, a gel becomes a fluid. *v*: to take the form of a gel; to set.

gone to water *adj*: pertaining to a well in which production of oil has decreased and production of water has increased (e.g., "The well has gone to water").

grapple *n*: a mechanism that is fitted into an overshot to grasp and retrieve fish from the borehole.

gravel *n*: coarse sand or glass beads of uniform size and roundness used in gravel packing.

gravel packing *n*: a method of well completion in which a slotted liner, often wire-wrapped, is placed in the well and surrounded by gravel. The mass of gravel excludes sand from the wellbore but allows continued production.

gravity drainage *n*: the movement of fluids in a reservoir resulting from the force of gravity. In the absence of an effective water or gas drive, gravity drainage is an important source of energy to produce oil, and it may also supplement other types of natural drive.

guide shoe *n*: 1. a short, heavy, cylindrical section of steel filled with concrete and rounded at the bottom, which is placed at the end of the casing string. It prevents the casing from snagging on irregularities in the borehole as it is lowered. A passage through the center of the shoe allows drilling fluid to pass up into the casing while it is being lowered and allows cement to pass out during cementing operations. Also called casing shoe. 2. a device, similar to a casing shoe, placed at the end of other tubular goods.

H

hang rods *v*: to suspend sucker rods in a derrick or mast on rod hangers rather than to place them horizontally on a rack.

headache *n*: (slang) the position in which the mast on a mobile rig is resting horizontally over the driver's cab.

hoisting system *n pl*: drawworks, drilling line, and traveling and crown blocks. Auxiliary hoisting components include catheads, catshaft, and air hoist.

horizontal drilling *n*: deviation of the borehole at least 80° from vertical so that the borehole penetrates a productive formation in a manner parallel to the formation. A single horizontal hole can effectively drain a reservoir and eliminate the need for several vertical boreholes.

horsehead *n*: the generally horsehead-shaped steel piece at the front of the beam of a pumping unit to which the bridle is attached in sucker rod pumping.

huff and puff *n*: (slang) see *cyclic steam injection*.

hydraulic *adj*: 1. of or relating to water or other liquid in motion. 2. operated, moved, or effected by water or liquid.

hydraulic fluid *n*: a liquid of low viscosity (such as light oil) that is used in systems actuated by liquid (such as the brake system in a passenger car).

hydraulic force *n*: force resulting from pressure on water or other hydraulic fluid.

hydraulic fracturing *n*: an operation in which a specially blended liquid is pumped down a well and into a formation under pressure high enough to cause the formation to crack open, forming passages through which oil can flow into the wellbore. Sand grains, aluminum pellets, glass beads, or similar materials are carried in suspension into the fractures. When the pressure is released at the surface, the fractures partially close on the proppants, leaving channels for oil to flow through to the well. Compare *acid fracture*.

hydraulic jar *n*: a type of mechanical jar in which a fluid moving through a small opening slows the piston stroke while the crew stretches the work string. After the hydraulic delay, a release mechanism in the jar trips to allow a mandrel to spring up and deliver a sharp blow. Compare *mechanical jar, rotary jar*.

hydraulic pumping *n*: a method of pumping oil from wells by using a downhole pump without sucker rods. A hydraulic pumping system consists of two pumps: one on the surface and one in the well. The surface pump drives the downhole pump by forcing clean crude oil (power oil) down the well through a tubing string. A mixture of power oil and produced fluid is returned to the surface.

hydrocarbons *n pl*: organic compounds of hydrogen and carbon whose densities, boiling points, and freezing points increase as their molecular weights increase. Although composed of only two elements, hydrocarbons exist in a variety of compounds, because of the strong affinity of the carbon atom for other atoms and for itself. The smallest molecules of hydrocarbons are gaseous; the largest are solids. Petroleum is a mixture of many different hydrocarbons.

hydrogen sulfide cracking *n*: a type of corrosion that occurs when metals are exposed to hydrogen sulfide gas; it is characterized by minute cracks that form just under the metal's surface.

I

immiscible *adj*: not capable of mixing (like oil and water).

impeller *n*: a set of mounted blades used to impart motion to a fluid (for example, the rotor of a centrifugal pump).

impermeable *adj*: preventing the passage of fluid. A formation may be porous yet impermeable if there is an absence of connecting passages between the voids within it. See *permeability*.

impression block *n*: a fishing accessory; a block with lead or another relatively soft material on its bottom that impresses a mirror image of the top of a fish; it also indicates the fish's position in the hole, i.e., whether it is centered or off to one side. From this information, the correct fishing tool can be selected.

induction log *n*: an electric well log in which the conductivity of the formation rather than the resistivity is measured. Because oil-bearing formations are less conductive of electricity than water-bearing formations, an induction survey, when compared with resistivity readings, can aid in determination of oil and water zones.

inflatable packer *n*: a packer with an element that inflates by means of gas or liquid pumped from the surface through a line. It is deflated by means of slots that can be opened to allow the gas or liquid to flow out. They are used when a temporary packer is needed in a hole with weakened casing that could be damaged by mechanical slips.

injection gas *n*: 1. a high-pressure gas injected into a formation to maintain or restore reservoir pressure. 2. gas injected in gas-lift operations.

injection log *n*: a survey used to determine the injection profile, i.e., to assign specific volumes or percentages to each of the formations taking fluid in an injection well. The injection log is also used to check for casing or packer leaks, bad cement jobs, and fluid migration between zones.

injection water *n*: water that is introduced into a reservoir to help drive hydrocarbons to a producing well.

injection well *n*: a well through which fluids are injected into an underground stratum to increase reservoir pressure and to displace oil. Also called input well.

injector head *n*: a control head for injecting coiled tubing into a well that seals off the tubing and makes a pressure-tight connection.

input well *n*: see *injection well*.

insert pump *n*: a sucker rod pump that is run into the well as a complete unit.

inside cutter *n*: see *internal cutter*.

in situ combustion *n*: see *fire flooding*.

intermediate casing string *n*: the string of casing set in a well after the surface casing but before production casing is set to keep the hole from caving and to seal off troublesome formations. Sometimes called protection casing.

internal cutter *n*: a fishing tool containing metal-cutting knives that is lowered into the inside of a length of pipe stuck in the hole to cut the pipe. The severed portion of the pipe can then be returned to the surface. Compare *external cutter*.

J

jackup *n*: a jackup drilling rig.

jackup drilling rig *n*: a mobile bottom-supported offshore drilling structure with columnar or open-truss legs that support the deck and hull. When positioned over the drilling site, the bottoms of the legs rest on the seafloor. A jackup rig is towed or propelled to a location with its legs up. Once the legs are firmly positioned on the bottom, the deck and hull height are adjusted and leveled. Also called self-elevating drilling unit.

jar *n*: a percussion tool operated manually or hydraulically to deliver a heavy downward blow to fish stuck in the borehole. *v*: to apply a heavy blow to the drill stem by use of a jar or bumper sub.

jar accelerator *n*: a hydraulic tool used in conjunction with a jar and made up on the fishing string above the jar to increase the power of the jarring force.

jar intensifier *n*: see *jar accelerator.*

jet *n*: in a perforating gun using shaped charges, a highly penetrating, fast-moving stream of exploded particles that forms a hole in the casing, cement, and formation.

jet cutoff *n*: a procedure for severing pipe stuck in a well by detonating special shaped-charge explosives similar to those used in jet perforating. The explosive is lowered into the pipe to the desired depth and detonated. The force of the explosion makes radiating horizontal cuts around the pipe, and the severed portion of the pipe is retrieved.

jet cutter *n*: a fishing tool that uses shaped charges to sever casing, tubing, or drill pipe stuck in the hole. See *jet cutoff.* Compare *chemical cutter.*

jet gun *n*: an assembly, including a carrier and shaped charges, that is used in jet perforating.

jet-perforate *v*: to create holes through the casing with a shaped charge of high explosives instead of a gun that fires projectiles. The loaded charges are lowered into the hole to the desired depth. Once detonated, the charges emit short, penetrating jets of high-velocity gases that make holes in the casing and cement for some distance into the formation. Formation fluids then flow into the wellbore through these perforations. See *bullet perforator, perforate.*

junk *n*: metal debris lost in a hole. Junk may be a lost bit, pieces of a bit, milled pieces of pipe, wrenches, or any relatively small object that impedes drilling or completion and must be fished out of the hole.

junk basket *n*: a device made up on the bottom of the fishing string to catch and retrieve pieces of junk from the bottom of the hole.

junk mill *n*: a mill used to grind up junk in the hole. See *mill.*

junk retriever *n*: a special tool made up on the bottom of the drill stem to pick up junk from the bottom of the hole. Most junk retrievers are designed with ports that allow drilling fluid to exit the tool a short distance off the bottom.

This flow of fluid creates an area of low pressure inside the tool so that the junk is lifted and caught in the retriever by the higher pressure outside the tool. See *junk, junk basket.*

junk sub *n*: see *boot sub.*

K

keyseat *n*: an undergauge channel or groove cut in the side of the borehole and parallel to the axis of the hole. A keyseat results from the rotation of pipe on a sharp bend in the hole.

kick *n*: an entry of water, gas, oil, or other formation fluid into the wellbore during drilling. It occurs because the pressure exerted by the column of drilling fluid is not great enough to overcome the pressure exerted by the fluids in the formation drilled. If prompt action is not taken to control the kick, or kill the well, a blowout may occur.

kickoff tool *n*: see *deflection tool.*

L

lease operator *n*: the oil company employee who attends to producing wells. He or she attends to any number of wells, ensures steady production, prepares reports, tests, gauges, and so forth. Also called a custodian, pumper, or switcher.

liner *n*: 1. a string of pipe used to case open hole below existing casing. A liner extends from the setting depth up into the intermediate casing or long string, usually overlapping about 100 feet (30.5 metres). Liners are nearly always suspended from the upper string by a hanger device. 2. a slotted liner.

liner completion *n*: a well completion in which a liner is used to obtain communication between the reservoir and the wellbore.

liner hanger *n*: a slip device that attaches the liner to the casing. See *liner*.

liner patch *n*: a stressed-steel corrugated tube that is lowered into existing casing in a well to repair a hole or leak in the casing. The patch is cemented to the casing with glass fiber and epoxy resin.

log *n*: a systematic recording of data, such as a driller's log, mud log, electrical well log, or radioactivity log. Many different logs are run in wells to discern various characteristics of downhole formation. *v*: to record data.

long string *n*: 1. the last string of casing set in a well. 2. the string of casing that is set at the top of or through the producing zone, often called the oil string or production casing.

lost pipe *n*: drill pipe, drill collars, tubing, or casing that has become separated in the hole from the part of the pipe reaching the surface, necessitating its removal before normal operations can proceed; a fish.

lubricator *n*: a specially fabricated length of casing or tubing usually placed temporarily above a valve on top of the casinghead or tubing head. It is used to run swabbing or perforating tools into a producing well and provides a method for sealing off pressure and thus should be rated for highest anticipated pressure.

M

macaroni rig *n*: a workover rig, usually lightweight, that is specially built to run a string of 3/4-inch or 1-inch (1.9- or 2.54-centimetre) tubing. See *macaroni string*.

macaroni string *n*: a string of tubing or pipe, usually 3/4 or 1 inch (1.9 or 2.54 centimetres) in diameter.

mandrel *n*: a cylindrical bar, spindle, or shaft around which other parts are arranged or attached or that fits inside a cylinder or tube.

mast *n*: a portable derrick that is capable of being raised as a unit, as distinguished from a standard derrick, which cannot be raised to a working position as a unit. For transporting by land, the mast can be divided into two or more sections to avoid excessive length extending from truck beds on the highway. Oil workers and manufacturers often use the words "mast" and "derrick" interchangeably. Compare *derrick*.

master gate *n*: see *master valve*.

master valve *n*: a large valve located on the Christmas tree and used to control the flow of oil and gas from a well. Also called master gate.

matrix acidizing *n*: an acidizing treatment using low or no pressure to improve the permeability of a formation without fracturing it. See *wellbore soak*. Compare *fracture acidizing*.

mechanical jar *n*: a percussion tool operated mechanically to give an upward thrust to a fish by the sudden release of a tripping device inside the tool. If the fish can be freed by an upward blow, the mechanical jar can be very effective.

mechanical log *n*: a log recording, for instance, rate of penetration or amount of gas in the mud, obtained at the surface by mechanical means. See *driller's log, mud logging*.

mill *n*: a downhole tool with rough, sharp, extremely hard cutting surfaces for removing metal, packers, cement, sand, or scale by grinding or cutting. Mills are run on drill pipe or tubing to grind up debris in the hole, remove stuck portions of drill stem or sections of casing for sidetracking, and ream out tight spots in the casing. They are also called junk mills, reaming mills, and so forth, depending on what use they have. *v*: to use a mill to cut or grind metal objects that must be removed from a well.

milling shoe *n*: see *rotary shoe*.

miscible *adj*: capable of being mixed.

miscible drive *n*: an additional recovery method in which a gas or liquid is injected into the reservoir to allow oil and water in the pores to mix and thus displace oil from the reservoir rock. See *chemical flooding, gas injection*.

motor *n*: a hydraulic, air, or electric device used to do work. Compare *engine*.

mud *n*: see *drilling fluid*.

mud acid *n*: a mixture of hydro-chloric and hydrofluoric acids and surfactants used to remove wall cake from the wellbore.

mud cake *n*: the sheath of mud solids that forms on the wall of the hole when liquid from mud filters into the formation. Also called filter cake or wall cake.

mud logging *n*: the recording of information derived from examination and analysis of formation cuttings made by the bit and of mud circulated out of the hole. A portion of the mud is diverted through a gas-detecting device. Cuttings brought up by the mud are examined under ultraviolet light to detect the presence of oil or gas. Mud logging is often carried out in a portable laboratory set up at the well.

mud motor *n*: see *downhole motor*.

multiple completion *n*: an arrangement for producing a well in which one wellbore penetrates two or more petroleum-bearing formations. In one type, multiple tubing strings are suspended side by side in the production casing string, each a different length and each packed to prevent the commingling of different reservoir fluids. Each reservoir is then produced through its own tubing string. Alternatively, a small-diameter production casing string may be provided for each reservoir, as in multiple tubingless completions. See *dual completion.*

multistage pump *n*: a stack of centrifugal pumps that develops pressure by means of impellers operating in series. Also called pump stage. See *electric submersible pumping.*

N

natural drive energy *n*: see *reservoir drive mechanism.*

neutron log *n*: any of several radioactivity well logs that records gamma rays released when a sonde bombards the formation with neutrons. See *radioactivity well logging.*

nitro shooting *n*: a formation-stimulation process first used about a hundred years ago in Pennsylvania. Nitroglycerin is placed in a well and exploded to fracture the rock. Nitro shooting has been largely replaced by formation fracturing.

nonferrous alloy *n*: alloy containing less than 50 percent iron.

nonporous *adj*: having no pores and therefore unable to hold fluids.

normal circulation *n*: the smooth, uninterrupted circulation of drilling fluid down the drill stem, out the bit, up the annular space between the pipe and the hole, and back to the surface. Compare *reverse circulation.*

nuclear log *n*: see *radioactivity log.*

nuclear tracer *n*: a gas, liquid, or solid material that emits gamma rays.

O

oil saver *n*: a gland arrangement that mechanically or hydraulically seals by pressure. It is used to prevent leakage and waste of gas, oil, or water around a wireline (as when swabbing a well).

oil spotting *n*: pumping oil, or a mixture of oil and chemicals, to a specific depth in the well to lubricate stuck drill collars.

oil string *n*: the final string of casing set in a well after the productive capacity of the formation has been determined to be sufficient. Also called the long string or production casing.

open formation *n*: a petroleum-bearing rock with good porosity and permeability.

open-hole completion *n*: a method of preparing a well for production in which no production casing or liner is set opposite the producing formation. Reservoir fluids flow unrestricted into the open wellbore. An open-hole completion has limited use in rather special situations. Also called a barefoot completion.

open-hole fishing *n*: the procedure of recovering lost or stuck equipment in an uncased wellbore.

open-hole log *n*: any log made in uncased, or open, hole.

operator *n*: the person or company actually operating an oilwell or lease, generally the oil company that engages the drilling, service, and workover contractors.

outside cutter *n*: see *external cutter.*

overshot *n*: a fishing tool that is attached to tubing or drill pipe and lowered over the outside wall of pipe or sucker rods lost or stuck in the wellbore. A friction device in the overshot firmly grips the pipe, allowing the fish to be pulled from the hole.

P

packer *n*: a piece of downhole equipment that consists of a sealing device, a holding or setting device, and an inside passage for fluids. It is used to block the flow of fluids through the annular space between pipe and the wall of the wellbore by sealing off the space between them.

packer flowmeter *n*: a tool for production logging that employs an inflatable packer. It ensures that all the fluid from the well passes through the measuring devices built into the tool.

packer fluid *n*: a liquid, usually salt water or oil, but sometimes mud, used in a well when a packer is between the tubing and the casing. Packer fluid must be heavy enough to shut off the pressure of the formation being produced, must not stiffen or settle out of suspension over long periods of time, and must be noncorrosive.

packer mill *n*: see *mill*.

packer squeeze method *n*: a squeeze cementing method in which a packer is set to form a seal between the working string and the casing. Another packer or a cement plug is set below the point to be squeeze-cemented. By setting packers, the squeeze point is isolated from the rest of the well. See *packer, squeeze cementing*.

packing *n*: a material used in a cylinder, on rotating shafts of a pump, in the stuffing box of a valve, or between flange joints to maintain a leakproof seal.

packing assembly *n*: the arrangement of the downhole tools used in running and setting a packer.

packing elements *n pl*: the set of dense rubber, washer-shaped pieces encircling a packer, which are designed to expand against casing or formation face to seal off the annulus.

packing fluid *n*: see *packer fluid*.

pack off *v*: to place a packer in the wellbore and activate it so that it forms a seal between the tubing and the casing.

paraffin *n*: 1. a type of hydrocarbon. See *hydrocarbon*. 2. a waxlike substance formed from heavier paraffin hydrocarbons. These heavier paraffins often accumulate on the walls of tubing and other production equipment, restricting or stopping the flow of the desirable lighter paraffins.

paraffin scraper *n*: a tube with guides around it to keep it centered in the hole, and a cylindrical piece with blades attached. Spaces between the blades allow drilling fluid to pass through and carry away the scrapings.

parallel strings *n pl*: in a multiple completion, the arrangement of a separate tubing string for each zone produced, with all zones isolated by packers.

parted rods *n pl*: sucker rods that have been broken and separated in a pumping well because of corrosion, improper loading, damaged rods, and so forth.

patch tool *n*: see *casing overshot*.

PDC log *abbr*: perforation depth control log.

perforate *v*: to pierce the casing wall and cement of a wellbore to provide holes through which formation fluids may enter or to provide holes in the casing so that materials may be introduced into the annulus between the casing and the wall of the borehole. See *bullet perforator, jet-perforate, perforating gun*.

perforated completion *n*: 1. a well completion method in which the producing zone or zones are cased through, cemented, and perforated to allow fluid flow into the wellbore. 2. a well completed by this method.

perforated liner *n*: a liner that has had holes shot in it by a perforating gun. See *liner*.

perforated pipe *n*: sections of pipe (such as casing, liner, and tail pipe) in which holes or slots have been cut before it is set.

perforating gun *n*: a device fitted with shaped charges or bullets that is lowered to the desired depth in a well and fired to create penetrating holes in casing, cement, and formation.

perforation *n*: a hole made in the casing, cement, and formation through which formation fluids enter a wellbore. Usually several perforations are made at a time.

perforation depth control log (PDC log) *n*: a combination of a radioactivity log that locates hydrocarbons behind the casing walls, run into the well with a collar locator that measures depth. Knowing the depth and the location of reservoirs helps the crew determine where to perforate the casing or liner.

perforator *n*: see *perforating gun*.

permanent packer *n*: a nonretrievable type of packer that is very reliable but must be drilled or milled out for removal.

permeability *n*: 1. a measure of the ease with which a fluid flows through the connecting pore spaces of rock or cement. The unit of measurement is the millidarcy. 2. fluid conductivity of a porous medium. 3. ability of a fluid to flow within the interconnected pore network of a porous medium.

pilot *n*: a rodlike or tubelike exten-sion below a downhole tool, such as a mill, that serves to guide the tool into or over another downhole tool or fish.

piloted mill *n*: see *pilot mill*.

pilot mill *n*: a special mill that has a heavy tubular extension below it called a pilot or stinger. The pilot, smaller in diameter than the mill, is designed to go inside drill pipe or tubing that is lost in the hole. It guides the mill to the top of the pipe and centers it, thus preventing the mill from bypassing the pipe. Also called a piloted mill.

pitman *n*: the arm that connects the crank to the walking beam on a pumping unit by means of which rotary motion is converted to reciprocating motion.

plastic squeezing *n*: see *chemical consolidation*.

plug *n*: any object or device that blocks a hole or passageway (such as a cement plug in a borehole).

plug back *v*: to place cement in or near the bottom of a well to exclude bottom water, to sidetrack, or to produce from a formation higher in the well. Plugging back can also be accomplished with a mechanical plug set by wireline, tubing, or drill pipe.

plug-back cementing *n*: a secondary-cementing operation in which a plug of cement is positioned at a specific point in the well and allowed to set. Compare *squeeze cementing*.

plunger *n*: 1. a basic component of the sucker rod pump that serves to draw well fluids into the pump. 2. the rod that serves as a piston in a reciprocating pump.

pole mast *n*: a portable mast constructed of tubular members. A pole mast may be a single pole, usually of two different sizes of pipe telescoped together to be moved or extended and locked to obtain maximum height above a well. Double-pole masts give added strength and stability. See *mast*.

polished rod *n*: the topmost portion of a string of sucker rods. It is used for lifting fluid by the rod-pumping method. It has a uniform diameter and is smoothly polished to seal pressure effectively in the stuffing box attached to the top of the well.

polymer flooding *n*: a type of miscible drive in which a polymer is injected into an injection well to allow oil and water to mix and flow to a producing well. See *miscible drive*. Compare *alkaline (caustic) flooding*, *chemical flooding*, *waterflooding*.

pore *n*: an opening or space within a rock or mass of rocks, usually small and often filled with some fluid (water, oil, gas, or all three).

pore pressure *n*: see *formation pressure*.

porosity *n*: 1. the condition of being porous (such as a rock formation). 2. the ratio of the volume of empty space to the volume of solid rock in a formation, indicating how much fluid a rock can hold. See *pore*.

portable mast *n*: a mast mounted on a truck and capable of being erected as a single unit. See *telescoping mast*.

potential test *n*: a test of the rate at which a well can produce oil or gas by measuring formation pressures.

power fluid *n*: in subsurface hydraulic pumping, the crude oil that is produced by a well, cleaned, and pumped back into the well to power the subsurface pump.

power sub *n*: a hydraulically powered device used in lieu of a rotary to turn the drill pipe, tubing, or casing in a well.

precipitate *n*: see *reaction products*.

preflush *n*: 1. fluid injected prior to the acid solution in an acid-stimulation treatment; sometimes called a spearhead. 2. an injection of water prior to chemical flooding that is used to induce reservoir conditions favorable to the surfactant solution by adjusting reservoir salinity and reducing ion concentrations. A preflush may also be used to obtain advance information on reservoir flow patterns.

pressure depletion *n*: the method of producing a gas reservoir that is not associated with a water drive. Gas is removed and reservoir pressure declines until all the recoverable gas has been expelled.

preventer *n*: shortened form of blowout preventer. See *blowout preventer.*

Primacord *n*: a textile-covered fuse with a core of very high explosive.

primary recovery *n*: the first stage of oil production in which natural reservoir drives are used to recover oil, although some form of artificial lift may be required to exploit declining reservoir drives.

production *n*: 1. the phase of the petroleum industry that deals with bringing the well fluids to the surface and separating, storing, measuring, and otherwise preparing them for transport. 2. the amount of oil or gas produced in a given period.

production casing *n*: the last string of casing set in a well, inside of which is usually suspended a tubing string.

production maintenance *n*: the efforts made to minimize the decline in a well's production. It includes, for example, acid-washing of casing perforations to dissolve mineral deposits, scraping or chemical injection to prevent paraffin buildup, and various measures taken to control corrosion and erosion damage.

production packer *n*: any packer designed to make a seal between the tubing and the casing during production.

production rig *n*: a portable servicing or workover rig, usually mounted on wheels and self-propelled. See *well-servicing rig, workover rig.*

production test *n*: a test of the well's producing potential, usually done during the initial completion phase.

production tubing *n*: a string of tubing used to produce the well, providing well control and energy conservation.

production well *n*: in fields which use injection wells, the well through which oil is produced. See *injection well.*

productivity test *n*: a combination of a potential test and a bottomhole pressure test the purpose of which is to determine the effects of different flow rates on the pressure within the producing zone of the well to establish physical characteristics of the reservoir and to determine the maximum potential rate of flow. See *bottomhole pressure test, potential test.*

proppant *n*: see *propping agent.*

propping agent *n*: a granular substance (sand grains, aluminum pellets, or other material) that is carried in suspension by the fracturing fluid and that serves to keep the cracks open when fracturing fluid is withdrawn after a fracture treatment.

pulling unit *n*: a well-servicing outfit used in pulling rods and tubing from the well. See *well-servicing rig.*

pulsed neutron logging device *n*: a measuring instrument run inside casing to obtain an indication of the presence or absence of hydrocarbons outside the pipe, to determine water saturation in a reservoir behind casing, to detect water movement in the reservoir, to estimate porosity, and to estimate water salinity.

pulsed-neutron survey *n*: a special cased-hole logging method that uses radioactivity reaction time to obtain measurements of water saturation, residual oil saturation, and fluid contacts in the formation outside the casing of an oilwell.

pump *n*: a device that increases the pressure on a fluid or raises it to a higher level. Various types of pumps include the bottomhole pump, centrifugal pump, hydraulic pump, jet pump, mud pump, reciprocating pump, rotary pump, sucker rod pump, and submersible pump.

pump barrel *n*: the cylinder or liner in which the plunger of a sucker rod pump reciprocates. See *sucker rod pump.*

pump-down *adj*: descriptive of any tool or device that can be pumped down a wellbore. Pump-down tools are not lowered into the well on wireline; instead, they are pumped down the well with the drilling fluid.

pumping unit *n*: the machine that imparts reciprocating motion to a string of sucker rods extending to the positive-displacement pump at the bottom of a well. It is usually a beam arrangement driven by a crank attached to a speed reducer.

pump jack *n*: a surface unit similar to a pumping unit but having no individual power plant. Usually, several pump jacks are operated by pull rods or cables from one central power source. Commonly, but erroneously, beam pumping units are called pump jacks. Compare *beam pumping unit.*

pump rate *n*: the speed, or velocity, at which a pump is run. In drilling, the pump rate is usually measured in strokes per minute.

R

radiation log *n*: see *radioactivity log*.

radioactivity log *n*: a record of the natural or induced radioactive characteristics of subsurface formations. Also called nuclear log. See *radioactivity well logging*.

radioactivity well logging *n*: the recording of the natural or induced radioactive characteristics of subsurface formations. A radioactivity log, also known as a radiation log or a nuclear log, normally consists of two recorded curves: a gamma ray curve and a neutron curve. Both help determine the types of rocks in the formation and the types of fluids contained in the rocks.

ram blowout preventer *n*: a blowout preventer that uses rams to seal off pressure on a hole that is with or without pipe. Also called a ram preventer. Compare *annular blowout preventer*.

ram preventer *n*: see *ram blowout preventer*.

range of load *n*: in sucker rod pumping, the difference between the polished rod peak load on the upstroke and the minimum load on the downstroke.

reaction products *n pl*: the compounds formed as a result of a chemical reaction, such as the reaction of an acid with rock. They may be solids (in which case they are called precipitates), liquids, or gases.

ream *v*: to enlarge the wellbore by drilling it again with a special bit.

reciprocating action *n*: back-and-forth or up-and-down movement, such as that of a piston in a cylinder.

reciprocating pump *n*: a pump consisting of a piston that moves back and forth or up and down in a cylinder. The cylinder is equipped with inlet (suction) and outlet (discharge) valves. On the intake stroke, the suction valves are opened, and fluid is drawn into the cylinder. On the discharge stroke, the suction valves close, the discharge valves open, and fluid is forced out of the cylinder.

recompletion *n*: after the initial completion of a well, the action and techniques of reentering the well and redoing or repairing the original completion to restore the well's productivity.

reeled tubing *n*: see *coiled tubing*.

refracturing *n*: fracturing a formation again. See *acid fracture, fracturing, hydraulic fracturing*.

reservoir *n*: a subsurface, porous, permeable rock body in which oil and/or gas has accumulated. Most reservoir rocks are limestones, dolomites, sandstones, or a combination. The three basic types of hydrocarbon reservoirs are oil, gas, and condensate. An oil reservoir generally contains three fluids—gas, oil, and water—with oil the dominant product. In the typical oil reservoir, these fluids become vertically segregated because of their different densities. Gas, the lightest, occupies the upper part of the reservoir rocks; water, the lower part; and oil, the intermediate section. In addition to its occurrence as a cap or in solution, gas may accumulate independently of the oil; if so, the reservoir is called a gas reservoir. Associated with the gas, in most instances, are salt water and some oil. In a condensate reservoir, the hydrocarbons may exist as a gas, but, when brought to the surface, some of the heavier ones condense to a liquid.

reservoir drive *n*: see *reservoir drive mechanism*.

reservoir drive mechanism *n*: the process in which reservoir fluids are caused to flow out of the reservoir rock and into a wellbore by natural energy. Gas drive depends on the fact that, as the reservoir is produced, pressure is reduced, allowing the gas to expand and provide the principal driving energy. Water drive reservoirs depend on water and rock expansion to force the hydrocarbons out of the reservoir and into the wellbore. Also called natural drive energy.

reservoir pressure *n*: see *formation pressure*.

reservoir rock *n*: a permeable rock that may contain oil or gas in appreciable quantity and through which petroleum may migrate.

resin *n*: a semisolid or solid mixture of organic compounds having no definite melting point or tendency to crystallize.

resistivity *n*: the electrical resistance offered to the passage of current; the opposite of conductivity.

resistivity log *n*: a record of the resistivity of a formation. Usually obtained when an electric log is run. See *resistivity well logging*.

resistivity well logging *n*: the recording of the resistance of formation water to natural or induced electrical current. The mineral content of subsurface water allows it to conduct electricity. Rock, oil, and gas are poor conductors. Resistivity measurements can be correlated to formation lithology, porosity, permeability, and saturation and are very useful in formation evaluation. See *electric well log*.

retrievable packer *n*: a packer that can be pulled out of the well when it fails, to be repaired or replaced.

reverse circulation *n*: the course of drilling fluid downward through the annulus and upward through the drill stem, in contrast to normal circulation in which the course is downward through the drill stem and upward through the annulus. Seldom used in open hole, but frequently used in workover operations. Also referred to as "circulating the short way," since returns from bottom can be obtained more quickly than in normal circulation. Compare *normal circulation*.

rework *v*: to restore production from an existing formation when it has fallen off substantially or ceased altogether. See *work over*.

rig *n*: the derrick or mast, drawworks, and rotating system for drilling or workover.

rig operator *n*: see *unit operator*.

rod *n*: see *sucker rod*.

rod blowout preventer *n*: a ram device used to close the annular space around the polished rod or sucker rod in a pumping well.

rod hanger *n*: a device used to hang sucker rods on the mast or in the derrick.

rod pump *n*: see *sucker rod pump*.

rod string *n*: a sucker rod string, i.e., the entire length of sucker rods, which usually consists of several single rods screwed together. The rod string serves as a mechanical link from the beam pumping unit on the surface to the sucker rod pump near the bottom of the well.

rotary helper *n*: a worker on a drilling or workover rig, subordinate to the driller, whose primary work station is on the rig floor. On rotary drilling rigs, there are at least two and usually three or more rotary helpers on each crew. Sometimes called floorhand, floorman, rig crewman, or roughneck.

rotary jar *n*: a type of mechanical jar whose jarring force is actuated and determined by rotating the work string; the more torque, the harder the jar. See *mechanical jar*.

rotary shoe *n*: a milling device attached to the bottom of washover pipe that mills debris accumulated around the outside of the pipe being washed over. Usually, a rotary shoe has pieces of very hard tungsten carbide embedded in it. Also called a burn shoe. See *washover pipe*.

S

safety joint *n*: an accessory to a fishing tool, placed above it. If the tool cannot be disengaged from the fish, the safety joint permits easy disengagement of the string of pipe above the safety joint. Thus, part of the safety joint and the tool attached to the fish remain in the hole and become part of the fish.

salinity log *n*: a special nuclear well log that produces an estimate of the relative amounts of oil, gas, or salt water in a formation. This log is electronically adjusted to reflect gamma ray emissions resulting from the collision of neutrons with chlorine atoms in the formations.

sand consolidation *n*: any one of several methods by which the loose, unconsolidated grains of a producing formation are made to adhere to prevent a well from producing sand but permit it to produce oil and gas.

sand control *n*: any method by which large amounts of sand in a sandy formation are prevented from entering the wellbore. Sand in the wellbore can cause plugging and premature wear of well equipment. See *gravel packing, sand consolidation, screen liner*.

sandfrac *n*: method of fracturing subsurface rock formations by injecting fluid and sand under high pressure to increase permeability. Fractures are kept open by the grains of sand.

sandline *n*: a wireline used on drilling rigs and well-servicing rigs to operate a swab or a bailer, to retrieve cores or to run logging devices. It is usually 9/16 inch (15 millimetres) in diameter and several thousand feet or metres long.

scale *n*: a mineral deposit (e.g., calcium carbonate) that precipitates out of water and adheres to the inside of pipes, heaters, and other equipment.

scraper *n*: any device that is used to remove deposits (such as scale or paraffin) from tubing, casing, rods, flow lines, or pipelines.

screening effect *n*: the tendency of proppants to separate from fracture fluid when the speed, or velocity, of the fluid is low.

screen liner *n*: see *wire-wrapped screen*.

screen pipe *n*: see *wire-wrapped screen*.

secondary recovery *n*: 1. the use of waterflooding or gas injection to maintain formation pressure during primary production and to reduce the rate of decline of the original reservoir drive. 2. waterflooding of a depleted reservoir. 3. the first improved recovery method of any type applied to a reservoir to produce oil not recoverable by primary recovery methods. See *primary recovery*.

self-elevating drilling unit *n*: see *jackup drilling rig*.

self-potential (SP) *n*: see *spontaneous potential*.

self-potential curve *n*: see *spontaneous potential curve*.

self-propelled unit *n*: see *carrier rig*.

sequestering agent *n*: a chemical used with an acid in well treatment to inhibit the precipitation of insoluble iron hydroxides, which form when the acid contacts scales or iron salts and oxides, such as are found in corrosion products on casing.

service company *n*: a company that provides a specialized service, such as a well-logging service or a directional drilling service.

service rig *n*: see *well-servicing rig*.

service well *n*: 1. a nonproducing well used for injecting liquid or gas into the reservoir for enhanced recovery. 2. a saltwater disposal well or a water supply well.

set casing *v*: to run and cement casing at a certain depth in the wellbore. Sometimes called set pipe.

set pipe *v*: see *set casing*.

set up *v*: to harden (as cement).

shaped charge *n*: a relatively small container of high explosive that is loaded into a perforating gun. On detonation, the charge releases a small, high-velocity stream of particles (a jet) that penetrates the casing, cement, and formation. See *perforating gun*.

shoot *v*: to explode nitroglycerin or other high explosives in a hole to shatter the rock and increase the flow of oil; now largely replaced by formation fracturing.

shot *n*: a charge of high explosive, usually nitroglycerin, detonated in a well to shatter the formation and expedite the recovery of oil.

Shooting has been almost completely replaced by formation fracturing and acid treatments.

shut-in bottomhole pressure *n*: see *formation pressure*.

sidetrack *v*: to use a whipstock, turbodrill, or other mud motor to drill around broken drill pipe or casing that has become lodged permanently in the hole.

single-pole rig *n*: a well-servicing unit whose mast consists of but one steel tube, usually about 65 feet (19.8 metres) long.

sinker bar *n*: a heavy weight or bar placed on or near a lightweight wireline tool. The bar provides weight so that the tool will lower properly into the well.

skid *n*: a low platform mounted on the bottom of equipment for ease of moving, hauling, or storing.

skin damage *n*: see *formation damage*.

slant-hole rig *n*: a drilling rig used to drill directional wells. See *directional drilling*.

sleeve *n*: a tubular part designed to fit over another part.

slick line *n*: see *wireline*.

slotted liner *n*: a relatively short length of pipe with holes or slots that is placed opposite a producing formation. Usually, it is wrapped with specially shaped wire that is designed to prevent the entry of loose sand into the well as it is produced. It is also often used with a gravel pack.

slug *n*: a quantity of fluid injected into a reservoir to accomplish a specific purpose, such as chemical displacement of oil.

slurry *n*: 1. in drilling, a plastic mixture of cement and water that is pumped into a well to harden. There it supports the casing and provides a seal in the wellbore to prevent migration of underground fluids. 2. a mixture in which solids are suspended in a liquid.

solution gas *n*: lighter hydrocarbons that exist as a liquid under reservoir conditions but that effervesce as gas when pressure is released during production.

solution-gas drive *n*: see *dissolved-gas drive*.

sonde *n*: a logging tool assembly, especially the device in the logging assembly that senses and transmits formation data.

sonic log *n*: a type of acoustic log that records the travel time of sounds through objects, cement, or formation rocks. Often used to determine whether voids exist in the cement behind the casing in a wellbore.

sonic logging *n*: see *acoustic well logging*.

sour corrosion *n*: embrittlement and subsequent wearing away of metal caused by contact of the metal with hydrogen sulfide.

SP *abbr*: spontaneous potential or self-potential.

spear *n*: a fishing tool used to retrieve pipe lost in a well. The spear is lowered down the hole and into the lost pipe. When weight, torque, or both are applied to the string to which the spear is attached, the slips in the spear expand and tightly grip the inside of the wall of the lost pipe.

Then the string, spear, and lost pipe are pulled to the surface.

spearhead *n*: see *preflush*.

spearhead overshot *n*: a small wireline-operated overshot designed to retrieve wireline.

speed reducer *n*: a set of gears installed between a prime mover and the equipment it drives to reduce the running speed. The speed reducer makes it possible to obtain the correct pump speed. Also called a gear reducer.

spent *adj*: in acidizing, describing acid which has reacted completely with the formation rock.

spinner survey *n*: a production logging method that uses a small propellor turned by fluid movement. By use of a recording arrangement, the number of turns of the propellor can be related to the fluid quantity flowing past the instrument to obtain a log of the amount of fluid flowing from a formation.

spontaneous potential (SP) *n*: one of the natural electrical characteristics exhibited by a formation as measured by a logging tool lowered into the wellbore. Also called self-potential or SP.

spontaneous potential (SP) curve *n*: a measurement of the electrical currents that occur in the wellbore when fluids of different salinities are in contact. The SP curve is usually recorded in holes drilled with freshwater-base drilling fluids. It is one of the curves on an electric well log. Also called self-potential curve.

spontaneous potential (SP) log *n*: a record of a spontaneous potential curve.

spot *v*: to pump a designated quantity of a substance (such as acid or cement) into a specific interval in the well.

squeeze *n*: a cementing operation in which cement is pumped behind the casing under high pressure to recement channeled areas or to block off an uncemented zone.

squeeze cementing *n*: the forcing of cement slurry by pressure to specified points in a well to cause seals at the points of squeeze. It is used to isolate a producing formation, seal off water, repair casing leaks, and so forth. Compare *plugback cementing*.

squeeze job *n*: a remedial well-servicing activity whereby a cement slurry is pumped into open perforations, split casing, or a fractured formation, to effect a blockage.

squeeze packer *n*: a downhole permanent, or drillable, packer that is set by lowering some of the weight of the tubing string onto the packer. The weight expands the packer's sealing element to prevent flow between the tubing string and the casing below the packer.

squeeze point *n*: the depth in a wellbore at which cement is to be squeezed.

squeeze tool *n*: a special retrievable packer set at a particular depth in the wellbore during a squeeze cementing job. See also *squeeze cementing*.

standing valve *n*: a fixed ball-and-seat valve at the lower end of the working barrel of a sucker rod pump. The standing valve and its cage do not move, as does the traveling valve. Compare *traveling valve*.

steam drive *n*: see *steam flooding*.

steam flooding *n*: a thermal recovery method in which steam is injected into a reservoir through injection wells and driven toward production wells. The steam reduces the viscosity of crude oil, causing it to flow more freely. The heat vaporizes lighter hydrocarbons; as they move ahead of the steam, they cool and condense into liquids that dissolve and displace crude oil. The steam provides additional gas drive. This method is used to recover viscous oils. Also called continuous steam injection or steam drive. Compare *cyclic steam injection, thermal recovery*.

stimulation *n*: any process undertaken to enlarge old channels or to create new ones in the producing formation of a well (e.g., acidizing or fracturing).

straddle packer *n*: two packers separated by a spacer of variable length. A straddle packer may be used to isolate sections of open hole to be treated or tested or to isolate certain areas of perforated casing from the rest of the perforated section.

straight hole *n*: a hole that is drilled vertically. The total hole angle is restricted, and the hole does not change direction rapidly—no more than 3° per 100 feet (30.48 metres) of hole.

stress concentrator *n*: see *stress riser*.

stress riser *n*: a notch or pit on a pipe or joint that raises the stress level and concentrates the breakdown of the metal structure. Also called a stress concentrator.

string *n*: the entire length of casing, tubing, sucker rods, or drill pipe run into a hole.

string shot *n*: an explosive method utilizing Primacord, which is an instantaneous textile-covered fuse with a core of very high explosive. It is used to create an explosive jar inside stuck drill pipe or tubing so that the pipe may be backed off at the joint immediately above where it is stuck.

string-shot back-off *n*: see *string shot*.

structural mast *n*: a portable mast constructed of angular as opposed to tubular steel members.

stuck pipe *n*: drill pipe, drill collars, casing, or tubing that has inadvertently become immovable in the hole.

stuck point *n*: the depth in the hole at which the drill stem, tubing, or casing is stuck. Also called freeze point.

stuffing box *n*: a device that prevents leakage along a piston, rod, propeller shaft, or other moving part that passes through a hole in a cylinder or vessel. It consists of a box or chamber made by enlarging the hole and a gland containing compressed packing. On a well being artificially lifted by means of a sucker rod pump, the polished rod operates through a stuffing box, preventing escape of oil and diverting it into a side outlet connected to the flow line leading to the oil and gas separator or to the field storage tank.

sub *n*: a short, threaded piece of pipe used to adapt parts of the drilling string that cannot otherwise be screwed together because of differences in thread size or design. A sub (i.e., a substitute) may also perform a special function.

submersible pump *n*: a pump that is placed below the level of fluid in a well. It is usually driven by an electric motor and consists of a series of rotating blades that impart centrifugal motion to lift the fluid to the surface.

sucker rod *n*: a special steel pumping rod. Several rods screwed together make up the mechanical link from the beam pumping unit on the surface to the sucker rod pump at the bottom of a well. Sucker rods are threaded on each end and manufactured to dimension standards and metal specifications set by the petroleum industry. Lengths are 25 or 30 feet (7.6 or 9.1 metres); diameter varies from 0.5 to 1.5 inches (12 to 30 millimetres). There is also a continuous sucker rod (trade name: Corod).

sucker rod pump *n*: the downhole assembly used to lift fluid to the surface by the reciprocating action of the sucker rod string. Basic components are barrel, plunger, valves, and hold-down. Two types of sucker rod pumps are the tubing pump, in which the barrel is attached to the tubing, and the rod, or insert, pump, which is run into the well as a complete unit.

sucker rod pumping *n*: a method of artificial lift in which a subsurface pump located at or near the bottom of the well and connected to a string of sucker rods is used to lift the well fluid to the surface. The weight of the rod string and fluid is counterbalanced by weights attached to a reciprocating beam or to the crank member of a beam pumping unit or by air pressure in a cylinder attached to the beam.

surfactant *n*: a soluble compound that concentrates on the surface boundary between two substances such as oil and water and reduces the surface tension between the substances. The use of surfactants permits the thorough surface contact or mixing of substances that ordinarily remain separate. Surfactants are used in the petroleum industry as additives to drilling mud and to water during chemical flooding.

suspending agent *n*: an additive used to hold the fine clay and silt particles that sometimes remain after an acidizing treatment in suspension; i.e., it keeps them from settling out of the spent acid until it is circulated out.

swab *n*: a hollow mandrel fitted with swab cups used for swabbing. *v*: to operate a swab on a wireline to lower the pressure in the wellbore and bring well fluids to the surface when the well does not flow naturally. Swabbing is a temporary operation to determine whether the well can be made to flow. If the well does not flow after being swabbed, a pump is installed as a permanent lifting device to bring the oil to the surface.

swab cup *n*: rubber or rubberlike device on a swab, which forms a seal between the swab and the wall of the tubing or casing.

swage *n*: a solid cylindrical tool pointed at the bottom and equipped with a tool joint at the top for connection with a jar. It is used to straighten collapsed casing or tubing and drive it back to its original shape.

sweet corrosion *n*: the deterioration of metal caused by contact with carbon dioxide in water.

T

tap *n*: 1. a tool for forming an internal screw thread. It consists of a hardened tool-steel male screw grooved longitudinally so as to have cutting edges. 2. a hole or opening in a line or vessel into which a gauge or valve may be inserted and screwed tight. *v*: 1. to form a female thread by means of a tap. 2. to extract or cause to flow by means of a borehole, e.g., to tap a reservoir.

taper tap *n*: a tap with a gradually decreasing diameter from the top. It is used to retrieve a hollow fish and is the male counterpart of a die collar. The taper tap is run into a hollow fish and rotated to cut enough threads to provide a firm grip and permit the fish to be pulled and recovered. See *tap*. Compare *die collar*.

telescoping mast *n*: a mast that can be erected as a unit, usually by a tackle that hoists the wireline or by a hydraulic ram. The upper section of a telescoping mast is generally nested (telescoped) inside the lower section of the structure and raised to full height either by the wireline or by a hydraulic system. Erroneously but commonly called a telescoping derrick.

temperature log *n*: a survey run in cased holes that measures the temperature in the hole. It is used to locate the top of the cement in the annulus because cement generates heat as it sets, or to locate where a fluid in the well is seeping into the formation or leaking through a hole in the casing.

temperature survey *n*: an operation used to determine temperatures at various depths in the wellbore. It is also used to determine the height of cement behind the casing and to locate the source of water influx into the wellbore.

tertiary recovery *n*: 1. the use of improved recovery methods that not only restore formation pressure but also improve oil displacement or fluid flow in the reservoir. 2. the use of any improved recovery method to remove additional oil after secondary recovery. Compare *primary recovery, secondary recovery*.

thermal recovery *n*: tertiary recovery processes that use heat to make reservoir oil more viscous. See *cyclic steam injection, fire flooding, steam flooding*.

tight formation *n*: a petroleum- or water-bearing formation of relatively low porosity and permeability.

tight sand *n*: sand or sandstone formation with low permeability.

tight spot *n*: a section of a borehole in which excessive wall cake has built up, reducing the hole diameter and making it difficult to run the tools in and out. Compare *keyseat*.

toolpusher *n*: an employee of a well service or workover contractor who is in charge of the rig and the entire service or workover crew. Also called a pusher, rig superintendent, or rig supervisor.

tracer *n*: a substance added to reservoir fluids to permit the movements of the fluid to be followed or traced. Dyes and radioactive substances are used as tracers in underground water flows and sometimes helium is used in gas. When samples of the water or gas taken some distance from the point of injection reveal signs of the tracer, the route of the fluids can be mapped.

tracer log *n*: a survey that uses a radioactive tracer such as a gas, liquid, or solid having a high gamma ray emission. When the material is injected into any portion of the wellbore, the point of placement or movement can be recorded by a gamma ray instrument. The tracer log is used to determine channeling or the travel of squeezed cement behind a section of perforated casing. Also called tracer survey.

tracer survey *n*: see *tracer log*.

trailer rig *n*: a heavier rig that may have a longer mast, a rotary, and one or two engines. The rig systems are powered by a prime mover.

traveling valve *n*: one of the two valves in a sucker rod pumping system. It moves with the movement of the sucker rod string. On the upstroke, the ball member of the valve is seated, supporting the fluid load. On the downstroke, the ball is unseated, allowing fluid to enter into the production column. Compare *standing valve*.

tree *n*: short for Christmas tree, which is the valves and fittings placed on top of a flowing well to control production.

truck-mounted rig *n*: a wellservicing and workover rig that is mounted on a truck chassis.

tubing *n*: relatively small-diameter pipe that is run into a well to serve as a conduit for the passage of oil and gas to the surface.

tubing head *n*: a flanged fitting that supports the tubing string, seals off pressure between the casing and the outside of the tubing, and provides a connection that supports the Christmas tree.

tubing pump *n*: a sucker rod pump in which the barrel is attached to the tubing. See *sucker rod pump*.

U

unconsolidated formation *n*: a loosely arranged, apparently unstratified section of rock.

unconsolidated sandstone *n*: a sand formation in which individual grains do not adhere to one another. If an unconsolidated sandstone produces oil or gas, it will produce sand as well if not controlled or corrected.

unit operator *n*: the oil company in charge of development and production in an oilfield in which several companies have joined to produce the field. Also called crew chief, rig operator.

unloading a well *n*: removing fluid from the tubing in a well, often by means of a swab, to lower the bottomhole pressure in the wellbore at the perforations and induce the well to flow.

V

viscosity *n*: a measure of the resistance of a fluid to flow. Resistance is brought about by the internal friction resulting from the combined effects of cohesion and adhesion. The viscosity of petroleum products is commonly expressed in terms of the time required for a specific volume of the liquid to flow through a capillary tube of a specific size at a given temperature.

viscous *adj*: having a high resistance to flow.

W

walking beam *n*: the horizontal steel member of a beam pumping unit that has rocking or reciprocating motion.

wash over *v*: to release pipe that is stuck in the hole by running washover pipe. The washover pipe must have an outside diameter small enough to fit into the borehole but an inside diameter large enough to fit over the outside diameter of the stuck pipe. A rotary shoe, which cuts away the formation, mud, or whatever is sticking the pipe, is made up on the bottom joint of the washover pipe, and the assembly is lowered into the hole. Rotation of the assembly frees the stuck pipe. Several washovers may have to be made if the stuck portion is very long.

washover *n*: the operation during which stuck drill stem or tubing is freed using washover pipe.

washover assembly *n*: see *washover pipe*.

washover pipe *n*: an accessory used in fishing operations to go over the outside of tubing or drill pipe stuck in the hole because of cuttings, mud, and so forth, that have collected in the annulus. The washover pipe cleans the annular space and permits recovery of the pipe. It is sometimes called washpipe.

washover shoe *n*: see *rotary shoe*.

washover string *n*: the assembly of tools run into the hole during fishing to perform a washover. A typical washover string consists of a washover back-off connector, several joints of washover pipe, and a rotary shoe.

washpipe *n*: see *washover pipe*.

water drive *n*: the reservoir drive mechanism in which oil is produced by the expansion of the underlying water and rock, which forces the oil into the wellbore. See *reservoir drive mechanism*.

waterflooding *n*: a method of improved recovery in which water is injected into a reservoir to remove additional quantities of oil that have been left behind after primary recovery. Waterflooding usually involves the injection of water through wells specially set up for water injection and the removal of water and oil from production wells drilled adjacent to the injection wells.

wellbore cleanup *n*: see *wellbore soak*.

wellbore soak *n*: a matrix acidizing treatment in which the acid is placed in the wellbore and allowed to react by merely soaking. It is a relatively slow process because very little of the acid actually comes in contact with the formation. Also called wellbore cleanup. See *matrix acidizing*. Compare *acid fracture*.

well completion *n*: the activities and methods of preparing a well for the production of oil and gas or for other purposes, such as injection; the method by which one or more flow paths for hydrocarbons are established between the reservoir and the surface.

well fluid *n*: the fluid, usually a combination of gas, oil, water, and suspended sediment, that comes out of a reservoir. Also called well stream.

well logging *n*: the recording of information about subsurface geologic formations, including records kept by the driller and records of mud and cutting analyses, core analysis, drill stem tests, and electric, acoustic, and radioactivity procedures.

well servicing *n*: the maintenance work performed on an oil or gas well to improve or maintain the production from a formation already producing. It usually involves repairs to the pump, rods, gas-lift valves, tubing, packers, and so forth.

well-servicing rig *n*: a portable rig, truck-mounted, trailer-mounted, or a carrier rig, consisting of a hoist and engine with a self-erecting mast. See *carrier rig*. Compare *workover rig*.

well stimulation *n*: any of several operations used to increase the production of a well, such as acidizing or fracturing. See *acidize, fracturing*.

well stream *n*: see *well fluid*.

whipstock *n*: a long steel casing that uses an inclined plane to cause the bit to deflect from the original borehole at a slight angle. Whipstocks are sometimes used in controlled directional drilling, in straightening crooked boreholes, and in sidetracking to avoid unretrieved fish.

wireline *n*: a small-diameter metal line used in wireline operations. Also called slick line. Compare *conductor line*.

wireline formation tester *n*: a formation fluid sampling device, actually run on conductor line rather than wireline, that also logs flow and shut-in pressure in rock near the borehole. A spring mechanism holds a pad firmly against the sidewall while a piston creates a vacuum in a test chamber. Formation fluids enter the test chamber through a valve in the pad.

A recorder logs the rate at which the test chamber is filled. Fluids may also be drawn to fill a sampling chamber. Wireline formation tests may be done any number of times during one trip in the hole, so they are very useful in formation testing.

wireline log *n*: any log that is run on wireline.

wireline logging *n*: see *well logging*.

wireline operations *n pl*: the lowering of mechanical tools, such as fishing tools, into the well for various purposes. Electric wireline operations, such as electric well logging and perforating, involve the use of conductor line, which in the oil patch is commonly but erroneously called wireline.

wireline service *n*: a general term used to refer to any servicing opera-tion using a wireline.

wireline survey *n*: a general term often used to refer to any type of log being run in a well.

wireline tools *n pl*: special tools or equipment made to be lowered into and retrieved from the well on a wireline, e.g., packers, swabs, gas-lift valves, measuring devices.

wireline well logging *n*: the recording of subsurface characteristics by wireline (actually conductor line) tools. Wireline well logs include acoustic logs, caliper logs, radio-activity logs, and resistivity logs.

wire-wrapped screen *n*: a relatively short length of pipe that has openings in its sides and a specially shaped wire wrapped around the pipe. It is used in wire-wrapped screen completions, usually in conjunction with a gravel pack. The screen and gravel pack block out sand and allow fluids to flow into the well through the openings in the screen. Also called a screen liner.

work over *v*: to perform one or more of a variety of remedial operations on a producing oilwell to try to increase production.

Examples of workover operations are deepening, plugging back, pulling and resetting liners, and squeeze cementing.

workover fluid *n*: a special drilling mud used to keep a well under control while it is being worked over. A workover fluid is compounded carefully so that it will not cause formation damage.

workover rig *n*: a portable rig, either trailer-mounted or a carrier rig, used for working over a well, consisting of a hoist and engine, mast, rotating system, pump, pits, and auxiliary equipment.

work string *n*: in drilling, the string of drill pipe or tubing suspended in a well to which is attached a special tool or device that is used to carry out a certain task, such as squeeze cementing or fishing.